HORNY
LIZARDS
and
Headless
CHICKENS

HORNY LIZARDS
and
Headless
CHICKENS

Everything you need to know about
our weird, wonderful and downright
disgusting world

Francesca Gould

piatkus

PIATKUS

First published in Great Britain in 2009 by Piatkus
Copyright © 2009 by Francesca Gould
The moral right of the author has been asserted

A CIP catalogue record for this book is available from the British Library

ISBN 978-0-7499-4233-5

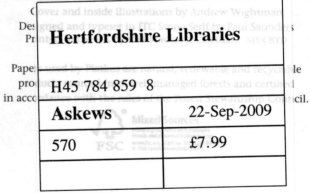

Cover and inside illustrations by Andrew Wightman
Designed and typeset in FTC Scala Serif by Paul Saunders
Pri...

Paper used by Piatkus are natural, renewable and recyclable
products and made from wood grown in sustainable, well managed forests and certified
in accordance with the rules of the Forest Stewardship Council.

Piatkus
An imprint of
Little, Brown Book Group
100 Victoria Embankment
London EC4Y 0DY

An Hachette UK Company
www.hachette.co.uk

www.piatkus.co.uk

This book is dedicated to Andrew Bedale and my
gorgeous daughter Sienna

Contents

Acknowledgements

I would like to thank Dr Richard Pollard, a highly amusing entomologist, who gave invaluable help regarding the eating of insects and, also, fig rolls.

CHAPTER ONE

Obscene cuisine

What is dancing-eating?

Dancing-eating or, to give it its proper name, *odorigui*, is the Japanese practice of eating live animals. One common *odorigui* dish is a small, transparent fish called *shirouo* that is served in alcohol and washed down with sake. More adventurous diners prefer to feast themselves on live octopus. To prepare this dish, the chef will remove the live octopus from a large tank, slice off one tentacle, and then simply serve it on a plate with some soy sauce. Apparently, the limb continues to writhe and twist on your plate; and when you eat it, the suckers attach themselves to the roof of your mouth.

However, the Japanese are not alone in their taste for very, very fresh meat. In China, there is a popular dish called 'drunken shrimp', which is also eaten live. When the dish arrives, it is swimming in a bowl of sweet alcohol, which is supposed to help make the shrimp a little less feisty and, because it's effectively in a drunken stupor, prevents it from escaping. The shrimp should be left to swim in the alcohol for about five minutes, before being eaten. The normal way to eat drunken shrimp is to remove it from the bowl, using chopsticks, and put in on a plate. The diner then removes the shrimp's head with their fingers, before munching on its twitching body. The Japanese also enjoy a similar dish called 'drunken crab'.

However, both these practices sound quite bland when compared with the extraordinary dish served at Pingxiang, on the border with Vietnam. Diners here buy live monkeys at the market, and then take them to a local inn to have them prepared by a chef. This preparation consists of forcing the monkeys to drink large amounts of rice wine, until they pass out. Then, the chef binds the monkeys' limbs, chops open their skulls and scoops out the brains into a bowl. Apparently, the test of a well-prepared monkey brain is that the blood vessels should still be pulsing when the dish is served. The brains are eaten with condiments including pickled ginger, chilli pepper, fried peanuts and coriander. It is said that monkey brain tastes like tofu, which rather begs the question: wouldn't it be simpler just to buy some tofu?

Which dish, properly prepared, should contain just enough poison to numb your lips?

The answer to this is the Japanese dish fugu, which is also known as the puffer fish or blowfish. Fugu is regarded as an exceptional delicacy in Japan, and many liken the taste to chicken, although it is eaten more for the thrill than the taste, as fugu contains one of most powerful poisons found in nature. The fish's traditional nickname is *teppo*, which means pistol.

In its natural environment, fugu is a peculiar-looking fish that can puff itself up into a large, round ball when threatened by predators. In addition, its main form of defence is the lethal poison contained in its internal organs, which is called tetrodotoxin. One blowfish contains enough tetrodotoxin to kill 30 adult humans.

Consequently, fugu chefs need to be exceptionally skilled and precise to ensure that all the poisonous parts of the fish are removed before serving. In Japan, fugu restaurants specialise in its preparation and the removal of the fish's deadly poison. If the fish has not been prepared correctly with all of its poison removed, the toxins can destroy the nerve tissue inside a person's body, paralysing the muscles necessary to breathe and causing death within about four to six hours. The most poisonous part of the puffer fish is the liver, which should be completely removed during preparation. Apparently, a skilled fugu chef will leave just enough poison to numb your lips. Even so, it's probably best not to annoy the chef.

Why is civet-poo coffee so expensive?

The world's most expensive coffee is an Indonesian speciality called *kopi luwak*, which is believed to be the best in the world; it is very popular in Japan and the US. Bizarrely, this coffee is made from beans that have been eaten and then excreted by the common palm civet.

The palm civet is a small, bobcat-like mammal that lives in certain rainforest regions of Indonesia. The palm civet's main diet consists of berries, insects and other small mammals, but it also enjoys eating coffee beans. However, not just any old coffee beans will do, the fussy civet chooses only the reddest and ripest beans. These beans then pass almost unchanged through the palm civet's digestive system, before being pooed out and then harvested by unfortunate plantation workers. They are then sold for ludicrous sums to wealthy coffee fanatics; to buy just 57g (2oz) of *kopi luwak* coffee, which is only enough to make one cup, costs around £25, making it a very expensive way to start your day!

But what is it that makes *kopi luwak* taste so good? There seem to be two main possibilities. The exceptional flavour may result from the effect of the civet's digestive juices on the coffee beans. Alternatively, these digestive juices may have no real effect; the answer may simply lie in the civet's fastidious pickiness in only selecting the very ripest, reddest coffee beans.

Which is the world's tastiest insect?

For centuries, many cultures around the world have been eating all sorts of insects and bugs. The practice even has a posh name: entomophagy. In some respects, insects make quite a good meal. They are widely available, easy to cook and highly nutritious; caterpillars, for example, are chock-full of protein and iron. Bugs that are commonly munched around the world include flies, beetles, dragonflies, grass-hoppers, cockroaches, butterflies, moths, mosquitoes, bee-tles, ants, and even bees and wasps. In fact, there are over 1,400 species of edible insects.

For example, in Nigeria, people enjoy snacking on crickets, which are disembowelled and then roasted over open coals. Grasshoppers are also popular, and people working the fields will often eat them raw. In China, a nice warming bowl of earthworm soup is believed to help treat fever. On the coast of Macao, you can buy a bag of fried cockroaches. Also, on the streets of Bangkok, in Thailand, fried grasshoppers are sold in much the same way.

In fact, people in Thailand eat a wide variety of insects including cicadas, locusts, mantises, deep-fried crickets, grasshoppers (usually fried), bamboo borers (these are small grubs, which are sometimes described on menus as 'fried little white babies'), steamed giant water bugs, weaver ants (which are eaten raw or rubbed with salt, chilli or pepper) and their eggs (these can also be eaten as a paste), dung beetles, moth and butterfly pupae, wasp and bee larvae, termite soup, and even the revolting-sounding grilled tarantula.

Meanwhile, in South America, tree worms and various stingless bees and wasps are widely eaten in Brazil. They are apparently known for their pleasant, almondy taste. In Columbia, culonas ants are also enjoyed for their nutty flavour. These winged ants are collected with large sweeping brooms, placed into boiling water, then taken out and dried on the grill. In the US, worker ants of this species are often dipped into chocolate.

Nor are Western countries immune from this kind of bizarre behaviour. One company in California makes products such as the Cricket Lick-It, which is a tasty, sugar-free lollipop with, you've guessed it, a real cricket in the centre. Perhaps you'd prefer the Scorpion Sucker, which comes in an array of colours and flavours, such as blueberry and banana, and contains, predictably enough, a scorpion. If you're not feeling that adventurous, how about a tasty snack of worms? These come in a variety of flavours, including barbecue, Cheddar cheese and Mexican spice.

Other products include the Antlix, a peppermint-flavoured lollipop that contains real farm-raised ants – apparently they taste similar to chilli peppers and are said to be good for giving you an energy boost. The Tequilalix is a tequila-flavoured lollipop, which contains a real worm. The Vodkalix is a vodka-flavoured lollipop, which, also for good measure, contains a scorpion. The scorpions are said to be heat-treated, to remove any toxins, to make sure they are safe to eat.

However, if I had to choose which insect would be the most delicious, I think I might plump for the Australian honey ant. This insect is greatly prized by the Aborigines, who call them by the rather appetising name of 'yarrumpa'. This insect stores so much of a sugary fluid in its body that its hind end swells up into a ball that is big enough to eat. People bite the bug's end off to savour the sweet stuff found inside. They say it's just like eating honey, only crunchier.

How do you make bird's nest soup?

The Chinese delicacy bird's nest soup is one of those rare dishes that sounds incredibly gross, but which is in fact far, far worse. This dish has been highly regarded since the time of the Ming dynasty (1368–1644), and it is said that there is no higher honour one can bestow upon a guest than to serve them bird's nest soup. This rare and expensive dish is prized for its rich nutrient content and purported health benefits and is made from the nests of a certain type of swift that live high up in the roofs of caves all over south-east Asia. The nests themselves are made from the birds' saliva that sets into a solid, rubbery substance.

Collecting the swifts' nests from the bat-filled caves is a very ancient and very dangerous job. Nest collectors have to climb up very high, and they use long bamboo poles to remove the nests that are found stuck to the roofs of the caves.

To make bird's nest soup, chefs simmer the nests in chicken broth for hours, until they become rubbery. Once cooked, the nests are said to be chewy and fairly tasteless, which is why flavourings such as chicken stock are often added. One reason why this culinary delight is so highly prized is because it is believed to be an aphrodisiac, as well as being beneficial for lung problems. For centuries, the Chinese have encouraged their children to eat the soup, believing it will help them to grow.

Who eats tarantula omelettes?

Despite its frightening appearance, the tarantula spider is regarded as a delicacy by a number of cultures around the world. For example, roasted tarantula is eaten by the Bushmen of central Africa, while people in northern Thailand reportedly like to strip off the spiders' legs and roast the bodies. Native peoples of South America also eat them. The

Piaroa Indians of Venezuela enjoy eating the big, hairy, bird-eating goliath tarantula, which has a leg span of 25cm (10in) and an abdomen the size of a tennis ball. The whole thing is the size of a dinner plate!

The Piaroa hunt for tarantulas, and when they've caught one, they bend its legs backwards over the body and tie them together, so it can be taken back to camp. To prepare the tarantula, a leaf is used to twist off the abdomen (to avoid touching the hairs, which can irritate the skin), and the spider is then rolled in a leaf and roasted in hot coals. Once it's cooked, the spider is eaten by picking out the bits of flesh, rather like eating a crab. Apparently, tarantula tastes a bit like prawns. Bits of the meat can get stuck between your teeth, but luckily the tarantula's long fangs make excellent toothpicks! If the Piaroa manage to catch a female tarantula, they will squeeze the eggs out from her body, wrap them in a leaf and roast them over a fire, to make a tarantula omelette.

The eating of spiders is also very popular in Cambodia and Laos, where they are commonly toasted on a bamboo skewer over a fire and served whole with salt or chillies. Alternatively, some people prefer their spiders fried in butter, with a clove of garlic.

Why did Nelson's sailors eat their biscuits in the dark?

In the 1700s, under Horatio Nelson's (1738–1805) leadership, Britain had the most powerful navy in the world. However, conditions on board were truly disgusting, and navy discipline was harsh. Floggings were frequent, the pay was low, hygiene was poor and the food was often infested with bugs.

Before setting off, ships would be loaded with food, including fruit, vegetables and live animals. However, once the ship departed, it wouldn't be long before all the animals had been slaughtered and the remaining food had rotted. As bread rapidly became mouldy, the sailors instead ate ship's biscuits, also known as 'hard tack', which were made with flour, water and salt. These biscuits would often contain weevils or maggots, so the sailors would tap the biscuits on the table, to try to knock most of the bugs out before eating. For this reason, many sailors would wait until dark to eat them, so they wouldn't have to see the maggots crawling inside.

The sailors' diet also included salted meat, which was so hard that it was practically inedible, even after being soaked and then boiled for hours. The meat was so dark and hard that some sailors developed a weird new craft: they would carve objects out of the meat and then polish their sculptures. Cheese was preserved by dipping it in tar, which made it taste disgusting. One of the main constituents of a sailor's diet was a healthy ration of a gallon of beer a day. Although beer did not keep aboard ship for very long, it was drunk as a safer alternative to water, as water on board the ship would quickly become green and slimy. A ten-year-old boy who served at the battle of Trafalgar wrote this letter home about the food, 'We live on beef which has been ten to eleven years in the cask and on biscuit which makes your throat cold in eating owing to the maggots which are very cold when you eat them, like calvesfoot jelly.'

However, there was of course some fresh food available from the surrounding waters, such as fish, dolphins, sharks and birds. Tortoises and turtles were also highly prized, as they could be kept alive for many weeks in the hold, without food or water, providing another source of fresh meat for the later stages of a voyage.

And God forbid that you should fall ill. According to Tobias Smollett, a ship's doctor during this period, the sick-bay on board was more likely to kill than cure. He wrote that patients were kept far below decks, deprived of daylight and fresh air, and breathing 'nothing but the morbid steams exhaling from their own excrement and diseased bodies, devoured with vermin hatched in the filth that surround them'.

What is the king of fruit?

The durian is a peculiar-looking, disgusting-smelling melon-like fruit, which is nonetheless considered a delicacy by millions of people in the Far East. In Indonesia, Malaysia, and especially Thailand, it is affectionately known as the king of fruit and, despite its disgusting smell, it is widely sold in south-east Asian markets.

The durian fruit can weigh as much as 4.5kg (10lb), and it has a hard green shell studded with spikes. The fruit grows at the top of durian trees, which can reach up to 50m (164ft) in height. As if this fruit were not unpleasant enough in its appearance and odour, it also presents a physical danger, as it has been known to drop from the branches and kill people below.

Apparently, the durian has a pleasant taste, which is described as being like a rich buttery custard, highly flavoured with almonds. Unfortunately, many people find the smell far too off-putting to consider actually tasting the thing. This smell is variously described as being like excrement, stale vomit, or even like a dead rat decomposing in a plate of vomit. Travel and food writer Richard Sterling memorably described the durian as smelling like 'pigshit, turpentine and onions, garnished with a gym sock'.

Because of the durian fruit's awful smell, the governments of many Asian countries have banned people from taking the fruit onto public transport. It is also banned by most hotels and airlines in the region, and rental car agencies will reportedly fine you if the car stinks of it when you hand in the keys.

More smelly plants

The world of nature contains numerous other putrid plants that are just as stinky and vile as the durian. For example, there is the flower of the exotic plant *Amorphophallus*, from Sumatra, which is also referred to as the corpse flower. This impressive plant has large petals and a phallus-like stem. It can reach a height of 2.4m (8ft), but its most notable feature is its nauseous stench, which has been described as a mixture of excrement and rotting flesh. The foul smell, which can be detected up to 1km (5/8 mile) away, is designed to attract flies, which help to pollinate the plant.

Aristolochia grandiflora, also known as the pelican flower, is found in Brazil and the Caribbean. This alien-looking plant has a huge flower, which can reach more than 1m (3ft 4in) in length. However, its smell is so disgusting that wild animals actually stampede from the area when the plant blossoms.

The flower *Rafflesia arnoldi* is named after Sir Thomas Stamford Raffles (1781–1826), who was the founder of Singapore. It is a huge, impressive-looking plant, with five mottled, orange-brown and white petals; the flower can measure up to 1m (3ft 4in) across. Unfortunately for Raffles, the smell of this flower has been described as being like rotten flesh, and because of this it is popularly known as the stinking corpse lily.

A pleasant amble through the woodlands of Europe or North America can quickly become disrupted if you come across a group of stinkhorns. These disgusting-smelling fungi grow in rotting wood, and they produce a smell that is said to be like decaying flesh. Their thick stalks, which grow to a height of around 25cm (10in), are capped with a liquid ball of a jellylike, foul-smelling green or brown slime. Flies and other insects that are attracted by the smell wallow in the slime, becoming covered with fungal spores. They then carry the spores when they fly away, and, in this way, help the stinkhorns to disperse.

How do you make a fly burger?

Lake Victoria in Africa is the second biggest freshwater lake in the world. At certain times of the year, peculiar dense clouds appear and hover over the lake. These clouds are made up of trillions of lake flies, which make up the largest swarm on Earth. These swarming flies are called *E sami* by the local people, and the clouds are visible on the horizon from miles away. Unfortunately, increased pollution and sewage are helping to increase their numbers.

Many of the flies reach land, and when this happens the air becomes thick with them, but the locals still carry on with their normal, daily lives. In fact, the flies are positively welcomed, as people take advantage of this blight by catching them for food. Entire villages will come together to catch the flies, using nets, baskets, pots and frying pans. One popular way of catching the flies is simply to dampen the inside of a pan – the flies stick to it and can then be cooked.

Each village has its own recipe, but one of the most

popular and widespread is the fly burger, which is also extremely nutritious. Fly burgers are made by crushing a handful of flies, which are then moulded into the shape of a burger and left to dry in the sun. The burger is then cooked – some regions like to roast them, while others enjoy their fly burgers deep-fried. Each burger contains around half a million flies, and seven times more protein than a beefburger.

What is a cod worm?

Have you ever been tucking into your fish and chips and noticed a worm inside your fish? If so, it was probably a type of round worm called a cod worm. Cod worms can grow to about 4cm (1½in) long, and they vary in colour from creamy white to dark brown. Although they are unsightly, they are actually quite harmless.

The life cycle of the cod worm is a fascinating and complex one. The adult worms live and mate inside the stomachs of grey seals, specifically grey seals that have eaten worm-infested fish. The cod worm's eggs pass out of the seals and into the ocean via their faeces. The eggs then hatch into tiny worm larvae, which get eaten by small crustaceans such as shrimps. In turn, these small crustaceans get eaten by larger sea creatures, including fish such as cod and haddock. As the cod worm larvae reach the fish's stomach, they continue to grow and eventually burrow through the stomach wall, into the flesh of the fish. Finally, the cod worm's life cycle comes full circle, when the fish is swallowed by another seal, and the process begins again.

Although it must be quite unpleasant to find a worm in your dinner, cod worms are relatively harmless. The worms are killed by cooking or freezing the fish, and there is no evidence that anyone has ever had an illness associated with the cod worm. Occasionally, when you buy fresh fish, you might even find a live cod worm inside it, but even so, although they're pretty gross, they are harmless if eaten. And the incidence of infected fish is very small in relation to the thousands of tons of fish landed each year.

What are sweetbreads?

Sweetbreads is a culinary term that refers to an animal's internal organs. The most commonly served sweetbreads are the thymus and pancreas glands of a calf, but chefs are also known to prepare the salivary and lymphatic glands. The thymus gland, which is known as the throat sweetbreads, is found near the base of an animal's neck. The pancreas, which we call the heart sweetbreads, is attached to the last rib – it lies near the heart. Generally, the throat sweetbreads of younger animals is preferred, because of its firm texture and delicate flavour. Sweetbreads can also be derived from lambs and pigs.

So why are they called sweetbreads? The most likely

answer seems to be simply that chefs realised that 'thymus' and 'pancreas' were not particularly appetising-sounding words on a menu, so instead they use the rather vague, pleasant-sounding term 'sweetbreads'.

What goes into a sausage?

After a pig has been slaughtered and the various cuts of meat such as hams and bacon have been taken away and processed, the remains of the carcass have other uses. The thymus gland and the pancreas can be used as sweetbreads. The intestines are used as casings for sausages. The trotters are sold fresh, and the pig's bones are used to make gelatine, which is used to thicken foods, such as yoghurts and sweets. The remaining edible parts of the pig, including snout, ears, face (including eyelids and lips), heart, kidneys, liver, stomach and tail, all end up in sausages.

> Laws are like sausages. It's better not to see them being made.
>
> Otto von Bismarck (1815–98), German statesman

Which dish contains six types of penis?

Most of us delicate Westerners would probably consider eating the genitals of an animal to be rather gross (unless it was part of a sausage, obviously), but not the Chinese. Some of these fearless gourmands choose to feast on animal penises, either steamed, roasted or boiled. Fans of this unusual branch of gastronomy say that penises have numerous health benefits: they are low in cholesterol, they boost a man's sex drive, and they are also helpful for treating all sorts of ailments – although these claims do not seem to have been fully embraced by the scientific community.

So where, you're no doubt wondering, can I sample this delightful Chinese cuisine? At China's first speciality penis restaurant, of course. As consuming a penis is supposed to help boost virility, you will find a predominantly male clientele at this establishment. It is common to see businessmen and government officials dining here, and these lucky chaps are able to sample the members of dogs, deer, yaks, oxen, donkeys, horses and even seals. One popular dish consists of a goat's penis, which is sliced, dipped in flour, fried and served on a skewer with soy sauce. Another favourite is the hotpot, which contains a range of samples of what the restaurant has to offer: six types of penis and four types of testicle, all expertly simmered in chicken stock.

Which cocktail contains a human toe?

In Canada, 65,000 hardy souls have joined the elite membership of the Sourtoe Cocktail Club, by drinking a very unusual cocktail, into which the barman places a preserved human toe. According to the rules of the club, to become a true Sourtoer, the drinker must allow the toe to touch his or her lips while drinking. Pass this test and you will receive a certificate to mark your achievement, as well as a story guaranteed to impress, or perhaps repulse, your friends and family for years to come.

So how did this bizarre practice start? And, more to the point, whose is the toe? According to the Sourtoe Cocktail Club (www.sourtoecocktailclub.com), there has been a succession of toes donated for this purpose.

The first toe belonged to trapper Louie Liken, for a time at least. In the 1920s, Liken became stuck in a blizzard with his brother Otto, and his big toe froze. To prevent the onset of gangrene, the toe would have to be amputated. However, Louie didn't trust doctors. He definitely didn't want to have to pay one, and, most certainly, he was not prepared to make the 97km (60 mile) journey to Dawson to find one. Instead, he drank as much rum as he could manage, to anaesthetise the pain, and then he got his brother to chop off the toe with his axe.

The toe was discovered many years later by Captain Dick Stevenson while cleaning the brother's cabin, and it was he who ingeniously came up with the idea of the Sourtoe Cocktail, and he started serving it at a hotel in Canada in 1973. However, in July 1980, a man called Garry Younger was trying for the Sourtoe record, and on his thirteenth glass of the cocktail, his chair tipped over backwards and he swallowed the toe. Of course, it was never recovered, so another one was needed.

Toe number two was donated by a lady called Mrs Lawrence, whose middle toe had been amputated many years before. The toe was kept in a jar of salt in the bar, but sadly got lost during a renovation.

Toe number three was donated by another trapper, who had had to have it removed due to frostbite. Unfortunately, in 1983, the toe was swallowed by a baseball player from the Northwest Territories. But not to worry because …

Toe number four was sent in by an anonymous donor, but was later stolen. The thief was identified but refused to give the toe back. Only when the police threatened to charge him with the transportation of human body parts across the border did he agree to return the pilfered digit.

Toes five and six were donated by another anonymous donor, with medical connections, who gave the toes on the condition that his nurses got to drink the Sourtoe for free. The fate of these toes is uncertain and for a time, the club didn't have a toe.

Toe number seven had been amputated from a diabetes sufferer, who decided to help out after reading about the Sourtoe plight in the newspaper.

And finally the most recent toe, toe number eight, was donated by a person who, as a result of a lawnmower accident, had their toe cut off while wearing open-toed sandals.

Do flies really puke on your food?

The common housefly is found in almost every part of the world. It will eat almost anything, including rotting vegetables, animal carcasses, excrement and vomit. This hairy six-legged insect's mouthparts comprise a proboscis, which is specially adapted for sucking up fluid or semi-fluid foods. The proboscis ends in a pair of oval-shaped fleshy labella, through which it sucks up the food.

However, the housefly can only suck up foods which are in something of a liquid state. This means that the fly has no problem sucking up thin fluids, such as milk or beer, or runny solids such as poo, spit, or mucus – the fly simply places its labella onto the food and sucks it up. However, when the housefly's dinner consists of something rather more solid, such as dried blood, cheese or cooked meats, it can't just suck these up. Instead, it has to moisten these foods, using either spit, or the regurgitated contents of a previous meal – perhaps some partially digested rotten rubbish or dog poo, for instance. As well as providing moisture, this fly vomit contains an acid that helps to dissolve whatever the fly has landed on, making it possible for the fly to hoover it up.

The housefly has three pairs of legs which end in claws and a pair of fleshy pad-like structures called the pulvilli, which contain tiny hairs. These sticky hairs enable the fly to stick to even very smooth surfaces, such as glass. The pulvilli are also responsible for picking up harmful germs when the fly lands on things like dog poo, mucus and rubbish. As a result, flies can carry more than a hundred disease-causing bacteria, including those that cause diarrhoea, cholera, typhoid and food poisoning.

What is maggot cheese?

Many of us enjoy cheeses that are riddled with mould, such as Stilton, but we would probably draw the line at a cheese infested with squirming maggots. But not the residents of Sardinia.

Casu marzu, which literally means rotten cheese, is a Sardinian tradition that more than lives up to its name. It is traditionally made with sheep's milk, into which flies have deliberately been allowed to lay thousands of eggs. When these eggs hatch, they produce translucent white worms, which grow up to around 8mm (1/3in) long. These worms produce a substance which causes the fat in the cheese to putrefy. The brown, decomposing cheese becomes a soft, sticky mass that creates a spicy, burning sensation in the mouth when eaten.

Eating insect-ridden food presents a range of new challenges. For one thing, the maggot larvae can leap for distances of up to 15cm (6in), and they have been known to jump into the cheese-eater's eyes. For this reason, casu marzu eaters often first seal the cheese in a bag before eating it. This starves the maggots of oxygen, causing them to leap out from the cheese and squirm at the bottom of the bag.

Because of the obvious health risks, casu marzu is officially outlawed in Italy, but it can still be bought on the black market. One official from the Sardinian health department stated that anyone caught selling the cheese would be heavily fined, but admitted, 'As a Sardinian and a man, let me tell you, I have never heard of anyone falling ill after eating this stuff. Sometimes, it tastes real good.'

Improving the flavour

Sometimes, extraordinary measures are taken to improve the flavour of cheese. In 1888, author J.G. Bourke received a letter from a doctor called Gustav Jaeger, which informed him about an unusual cheese that had been sold in Berlin. Apparently, a storekeeper was punished when it was revealed that he had been using the urine of young girls to make his cheese richer and tastier. It was said that the cheese had proved very popular, and people had loved the taste.

What are one-hundred-year-old eggs?

China's cuisine is not for the faint-hearted. From the skinned dogs displayed at markets, to the scorpion kebabs sold by traders, the Chinese display an admirably open-minded approach to food, which puts our prissy Western palates to shame. So, it's no surprise to find that they also enjoy eating a dish called *pi-tan*, which is also known as one-hundred-year-old eggs. Despite the rather attention-seeking name, *pi-tan* eggs are actually only four years old, and they are considered a great delicacy.

To make *pi-tan*, the Chinese usually use duck eggs that are left to soak in a mixture containing salt, lime and tea leaves, for three months. After this, the eggs are then coated with a paste of clay, lime, ashes and salt, and buried in the ground. They are left there for three or four years. Then the eggs are dug up and peeled to reveal a green, cheesy yolk and a yellow, gelatinous egg white. The raw, foul-smelling egg is then dipped in vinegar and eaten.

What is 'tapping the Admiral'?

In 1805, Admiral Horatio Nelson died during the battle of Trafalgar on his ship, the *Victory*, and subsequently his body was shipped home to England for burial. There is a common mistaken belief that Nelson's body was transported back to England in a keg of rum. For that reason, to this day, rum is colloquially known as 'Nelson's Blood'.

However, it was in fact brandy, not rum, that preserved Nelson's body on the long journey back to England. At this time, most sailors who died at sea would also be buried at sea, so preserving Nelson's body presented an unusual challenge. It was the idea of the ship's doctor, Dr Beatty, to preserve Nelson's body by storing it in a barrel of brandy. According to legend, when the barrel was opened on the ship's return to England, most of the brandy was gone. Apparently, the sailors on board had been tapping the barrel for drinks of brandy, and this is where the saying 'tapping the Admiral' – which means illicit drinking – comes from.

CHAPTER TWO

Weird creatures

Why does the horned lizard squirt blood from its eyes?

In 1960, American cinema audiences were scared witless by the astonishingly realistic dinosaurs in the film *The Lost World*. In fact, what appeared to be enormous, snarling predators were actually horned lizards, which are small lizards just a few inches long, but which were filmed using powerful magnification. There are 13 species of horned lizard found in North America; they have a broad body and rough skin, with horns on their head and spines across their back. Although they look quite frightening, horned lizards are usually docile and passive unless provoked, and they have a rather gross way of fending off predators.

Despite their spiky, unappetising appearance, horned lizards are preyed upon by a wide range of creatures including hawks, roadrunners, snakes, dogs, wolves, coyotes and other lizards. To defend themselves against these numerous threats, the horned lizard has developed a number of remarkable and unusual talents. When faced with a hungry predator, it is able to inflate itself with air, so that it resembles a spiky balloon, making it look bigger and more threatening.

If this doesn't work, the lizard can employ another bizarre technique: shooting blood from its eyes. To do this, it arches its back defensively and closes its eyes. The blood pressure inside the lizard's head quickly rises, and this pressure causes blood vessels in the sinuses to rupture. Then, the lizard's eyeballs becomes infused with blood and swell up, causing the eyelids to bulge. Finally, the swollen eyelids, engorged with blood, send out a fine spray of blood, through the tear ducts. They can shoot blood from either one or both eyes, up to a distance of 1.8m (6ft), and they can even direct the spray forwards or backwards.

So what's the point of this extraordinary ability? Well, firstly, the blood squirting serves to alarm and confuse would-be predators, naturally enough. Another benefit is that the stream of blood contains a chemical that is noxious to dogs, wolves and coyotes. If any of these animals gets the blood in its mouth, it shakes its head vigorously from side to side, as it finds the substance so repulsive.

However, despite having these spectacular talents, the horned lizard's most effective way of avoiding predators is simply to lie still. The lizard's colouring is similar to that of the soil on which they live, and they can eliminate any shadows by flattening their bodies against the ground. If they have to move, they can run and then stop suddenly and unexpectedly, lying flat to merge into their surroundings, leaving the predator scratching its head, wondering where its dinner went.

Which worm may crawl out of your nose?

Worldwide, around 1.4 billion people have got one or more ascaris worms living inside them. However, they rarely cause a problem, so people don't realise they're playing host to an uninvited guest. The most commonly encountered parasitic worm is the roundworm, which can measure 15–35cm (6–14in) in length, making it about the size of an earthworm. So how do they find their way into our bodies? The eggs of ascaris are transmitted in faeces, and they find their way into a new host via food or dirty fingers.

Once inside the body, the eggs hatch into larvae within a person's stomach, before moving into the small intestine. They then penetrate through the intestinal wall, enter the blood circulation and are carried around the body. The larvae make their way to the lungs, and as they continue to climb, the young ascaris larvae tend to irritate the airways slightly as they crawl up the back of the throat, which can cause a cough reflex, resulting in a free ride into the throat. However, occasionally adult worms can be coughed up into the mouth too, which gives the sufferer quite a shock. From the throat, the larvae are swallowed, which brings them to the intestines, where they make their home, and here they grow into adult worms.

Adult worms can live in a person's gut for around 6–24 months, and many people are unaware of their infestation until they see an adult worm in their poo, or cough up an adult worm. The worms have even also been known to come out of a person's nose or in their vomit. In severe cases, where people host many worms, the victim may suffer from anaemia or even malnutrition. Fortunately, the ascaris worm is extremely rare in the UK. However, in the US it is estimated to affect four million people.

Which fish uses slime to kill its enemies?

When a creature has not one disgusting name, but two, the odds are against it being a cute, doe-eyed bundle of fur. Such is the case with the hagfish, also known as the slime eel; it is every bit as disgusting as these names suggest. The hagfish is an ancient creature that has been around for 300 million years. It is virtually blind and resembles an over-sized, slimy worm. It is completely covered in mucus that oozes out of hundreds of slime pores found on the sides of its body.

The hagfish hangs around on the bottom of the ocean floor and looks for fish that are either sick or dead. It then climbs inside its prey, through the mouth, gill, eye socket, or anus, and devours it from the inside out, using its tooth-covered tongue to scrape its victim to pieces. The hagfish's mouth is very unusual and extremely ugly. It is surrounded by four pairs of tentacles, with a single tooth on the roof of the mouth and a tongue covered with two rows of strong, pointy teeth.

When faced with a predator, the hagfish uses its glands to produce a substantial amount of slime that quickly turns the surrounding water thick and gunky. This slime surrounds the predator, protecting the hagfish. The thick slime can even kill the predator, by clogging up its gills and suffocating it. However, there is a delicate balance to be struck, as the hagfish must be careful not to produce too much mucus, as it can suffocate itself instead. Hagfish slime is a unique substance, made from protein, which is best described as a kind of rubbery snot. When the hagfish thinks that the predator has been seen off and the coast is clear, it will tie itself into knots to rub away the excess slime.

Fishermen consider hagfish a nuisance, because they penetrate the bodies of fish caught in the fishermen's nets and eat them from the inside out, leaving nothing but skin and bones. One large fish was found with over 100 hagfish munching inside it.

What is the hagfish's even uglier cousin?

A close relative of the hagfish is the lamprey. The lamprey has a slimy eel-like body and can grow up to 1.2m (4ft) in length. It has two fins along its back and a single nostril in the middle of the head, but its mouth is even more unpleasant. The lamprey's large funnel-like mouth is very round, with rows of razor-sharp teeth, a sharp tongue and lips that also bear many rasping teeth. Unlike the hagfish, the lamprey chooses healthy creatures to feed upon, including human beings.

When a lamprey comes across a potential victim, which could be another fish, or a swimmer with cold legs, it attacks by attaching itself. The lamprey's sucking lips close upon the skin of the victim, and its sharp teeth scrape open a wound. The lamprey has a special type of saliva which stops the prey's blood from clotting. Then, the toothed tongue goes into action, lapping the blood and body fluids of the victim. Once the lamprey has eaten its fill, it lets go. The victim doesn't die from the bite itself, but it bears a wound that may become infected. Where lampreys are common, a single host fish may have several lampreys attached to it at one time. And if a fish suffers too many lamprey attacks, it may become weak and die. Infected lamprey bites cause the deaths of many fish in the ocean and the Great Lakes in the US. However, human victims are fairly rare, with no recorded fatalities.

Which animal is the best actor?

One of nature's most impressive and convincing performances is that given by the opossum, a small mammal found
throughout the US. Opossums usually live in woodland
and grow to about 51cm (20in) long, and are mostly grey-
coloured, with a white, pointed face and a tail like a rat's,
but bigger. They are active at night and will eat almost anything: insects, snails, toads, rodents and even dead animals.

The main threats faced by opossums are dogs, cats, foxes
and people. When they feel threatened, opossums will hiss
and bare their many sharp teeth. If this doesn't work, they
may use their considerable acting skills, by playing dead.
The opossum will flop down on its side, lying still, with its
eyes half-closed and its mouth hanging open with its
tongue lolling out. If required, it can play dead for several
hours; even if it is poked or kicked it will not move a muscle.
For added verisimilitude, the opossum may even defecate
on itself, as well as releasing a foul-smelling green slime
from its anus that smells like rotting flesh. Most of the
opossum's predators will not eat animals that are already
dead, so they leave the stinking opossum alone.

Why do skunks stink?

The skunk is a member of the weasel family that is commonly found in North America. Skunks rarely attack unless
they are cornered or are defending their young. But if a
skunk does feel threatened and is unable to escape, it will
put on an aggressive display by growling, fluffing up its fur,

shaking its tail, stamping the ground with its front feet, standing on its hind legs and spitting violently – all of which will hopefully serve to frighten and discourage the potential attacker. However, if those methods don't work and the predator remains a threat, the skunk will lift up its tail and spray.

The chemical skunks spray at their enemies is a sulphur compound called N-bulymercaptan, which burns the attacker's skin and causes stinging in the eyes, making the predator blind for a short while. The skunk sprays this disgusting, noxious chemical in a fanlike pattern, from two small openings inside its anus, which act rather like tiny water pistols. The glands that produce N-bulymercaptan hold enough for five or six full-powered sprays. A skunk can aim this spray by twisting the nozzles in all directions, but they seldom spray without being provoked or giving warning. The skunk's spray is extremely accurate, and effective at a range of up to 4.6m (15ft). As a result, even though skunks have sharp teeth, they rarely use them in defence.

If it gets into a person's eyes, skunk spray is extremely irritating, and can cause temporary blindness, but no permanent damage.

Which wasp lays its eggs inside a caterpillar?

There is a tiny wasp called *Cotesia congregata*, commonly found in the US, that has a deeply unpleasant, albeit fiendishly clever way of helping her eggs to hatch; it also ensures the little ones have a ready-made meal waiting for them.

The victim of this unpleasant practice is a large green caterpillar commonly known as the tobacco hornworm. Because of its green colour, this caterpillar is often overlooked by predators when hidden in a plant's leaves. But, the wasp hunts by smell and the smell of the caterpillar's faeces gives it away, guiding the wasp to its prey. It then lands on the back of the caterpillar, punctures its hide and injects as many as several hundred eggs into the victim's body, using its tube-like stinger. A few days later, wasp larvae emerge from the eggs and begin to grow. As the larvae near maturity, they chew their way through the body of the dying caterpillar.

However, there is a danger that the caterpillar's potent defences could kill the wasp's offspring, so the wasp has to disable them. Furthermore, the wasps must do this without killing the caterpillar, otherwise the wasp larvae will die too. Therefore, the wasps need to keep the caterpillar alive, but defenceless. To achieve this, when laying her eggs the wasp injects the caterpillar with venom that includes a debilitating virus. This virus produces toxic proteins that impair the caterpillar in a number of ways. The most important of these is to disable the caterpillar's immune system and hamper its physical growth, making it easier for the wasp larvae to take over. Gross, but clever!

Is it true that a cockroach farts every 15 minutes?

There are over 3,500 types of cockroaches, of all shapes and sizes. The hissing cockroach from Madagascar is as big as a mouse, while the smallest cockroaches are the size of a tomato seed. Until recently, a beast called the giant burrowing cockroach held the record for the world's largest roach. This wingless cockroach, which bizarrely, is a popular pet in Australia, grows up to 9cm (3½in) long (about the size of an adult finger), and weighs more than 44g (1½oz) – about the weight of an AA battery. Despite its large size, it's able to flatten its body so that it can fit into the smallest spaces. However, in 2004, scientists exploring caves in Borneo discovered a new species of cockroach; the monster roach measured 10cm (4in) long. This new discovery has taken over as the world's largest roach, in terms of size, although the giant burrowing cockroach is still the world's heaviest.

Cockroaches have teeth in their stomachs and will eat just about anything. They will happily eat the toe jam on your feet (dead skin cells, sock fluff, surface dirt, sweat, skin oils and bacteria which tend to collect between a person's toes throughout the day), the moisture in your nostrils, your armpit sweat, even their own skins or other cockroaches – they really aren't fussy. The American cockroach is a large, brown, winged cockroach about 4cm (1½in) long. It is commonly found in the southern US and in tropical climates, and often lives in sewers. It will eat practically anything, including leather, bookbindings, soap, glue and flakes of dead skin. It has also been known to munch on the eyelashes, eyebrows, fingernails and even the toenails of people while they sleep. Grossly, as cockroaches eat their food, they also poo on it and then trample it over their next meal. All sorts of harmful germs are found in their faeces and can cause illnesses in humans such as diarrhoea, typhoid, lung problems and urinary tract infection.

Cockroaches also have other gross habits – they love to fart, and on average break wind every 15 minutes. They also continue to release stinky methane gas for 18 hours after they die. Insects called termites also fart a great deal and, along with cockroaches, are believed to be among the biggest contributors to global warming.

Cockroaches are also some of nature's hardiest creatures. Some species of cockroach can survive in blazing heat, whereas others can endure being frozen, then thawed and still crawl away unharmed. Some cockroaches can go without food for three weeks. This astonishing creature can even survive, after being decapitated, for up to nine days, as it can breathe through a series of tubes attached to small openings on its body, which allow oxygen to pass to its cells. However, eventually it dies from starvation!

Which animal removes its own stomach to feed?

The common starfish is not actually a fish, but an echinoderm, which is closely related to other species such as sea urchins. The common starfish can grow up to 1m (3ft 4in) across; it has five arms, each of which contains tiny suckers, and a central mouth underneath the upper body. However, there are some species which have as many as 40 arms. Starfish mostly live in the Atlantic Ocean, but are also found in the Mediterranean Sea.

Starfish feed on clams, mussels, oysters and worms; and when they've found their food, such as a clam, they put their arms around it and grip it with their suckers, which gradually pull the victim's shell apart. The starfish then pushes its whole stomach out of its mouth and into the shell of the prey. Once inside, the stomach releases digestive juices and begins to slowly digest the clam. When it has finished its meal, it sucks its stomach back into its body through its mouth.

Starfish are extraordinary creatures in many ways. When they are attacked, some may lose an arm or two; however, this isn't a problem because they can simply regenerate new arms. Most species must have the central part of the body intact to be able to regenerate, but a few can grow an entire new starfish from a single arm. Before this was known, fishermen would cut starfish into pieces thinking it would kill them, but the pieces grew into new starfish, and so their population increased dramatically.

To reproduce, males and females release clouds of sperm and eggs respectively into the water, and fertilisation takes place there, which is something to bear in mind when swimming in the sea.

Why do male hippos shower each other in faeces and urine?

Most of the world's hippopotamuses are found in Africa, and can weigh as much as 3,356kg (3½ tons). They spend most of their time in water where they defecate in copious amounts. The dung is important for the food chain as it contains important nutrients for many microorganisms, which are in turn eaten by fish.

Around the river Nile, male hippos mark off their territorial boundaries by performing a disgusting ritual. As the hippo walks, it defecates, and as it does so it spins its tail to distribute the excrement over the largest possible area. Hippos also urinate backwards, probably for the same reason. At night, they leave their rivers and lakes to graze on grasslands. To ensure that they can find their way back to the water, they mark their route by leaving piles of dung; the smell helps them to follow their trail.

Also, to indicate their status, dominant males will stop and stare at each other, then turn backside to backside and shower each other in urine and faeces propelled with the help of their paddling tails, before walking away from each other. This behaviour may seem gross, but it does at least provide a snack for nearby baboons.

Which frog gives birth through its mouth?

Frogs tend to lay a large number of eggs in order to maximise the odds of survival, because there are many hazards between an egg being fertilised and becoming a full-grown frog. However, some frogs have some very unusual ways of helping to ensure their offspring get the best possible start in life.

Male Darwin's frogs attract the female frogs by singing to them. After this romantic courtship, the female leaves the male to watch over the eggs. He gathers them up and swallows them, storing them in his vocal sac. Here, the eggs develop into tiny frogs, before being spat out into the world.

Another amazing frog was the Australian gastric brooding frog, which sadly was only discovered just before it became extinct. This fascinating creature would lay its eggs in the water, where they would be fertilised by the male, and then swallowed by the female. Inside the female's stomach, the eggs would develop into tadpoles, before emerging as baby froglets five weeks later from the mother's mouth.

But perhaps the most bizarre frog reproductive method is that of the brightly coloured strawberry dart-poison frog. This amazing tiny frog first lays five to ten eggs on a horizontal leaf, which both the male and female visit regularly, but the male has the job of keeping the eggs moist by urinating on them until they hatch. Then, when the eggs develop into tadpoles, the mother places them individually into small pools of water (because they are cannibalistic) and provides them with eggs that have failed to fertilise to feed on.

Why do herring fart?

Some fish, such as the male cod, are known to produce a kind of grunting or buzzing noise to attract females, but these noises are not really farts as they are not produced by the fish's anus. Instead, the male cod makes this noise by vibrating an air-filled sac called a swim bladder. This lies beneath its backbone and is used to control the fish's buoyancy.

However, one fish which does fart is the herring, which does so in a fascinating way, which seems to be unique to this species. It seems that herring make farting sounds to let each other know where they are, and these noises are so high pitched that only other herring are able to hear them. No other fish has been known to make noises from its anus or to produce such a high-pitched noise.

'It sounds just like a high-pitched raspberry,' says research leader Ben Wilson of the University of British Columbia in Vancouver. Wilson and his team cannot be sure why herring make this sound, but believe that it might explain the enigma of how herring shoals stay together at night. Originally, biologists thought that the high-pitched sounds were produced by the herring's swim bladder. However, they then noticed a fine stream of bubbles always accompanied the farting noise from the fish's anus. 'In video pictures we can see the bubbles coming out of the anal duct at the same time,' says Robert Batty, senior research scientist at the Scottish Association for Marine Science in Oban.

The University of British Columbia team, which clearly had a sense of humour, called this noise fast repetitive tick, or FRT for short. Wilson remarked that the number of FRTs produced does not change when the fish are fed. Also, if the fish were starved they still produced the sounds. One other theory was that the FRTs were produced out of fear, but this too was rejected. The herring did not appear to be farting out of fear, because when they were exposed to shark scent there was again no noticeable increase in bubbles or sound.

The researchers eventually became convinced that the FRTs were most likely produced for the purpose of communication, for three reasons. Firstly, they noticed that more FRTs were produced when the herring were in bigger shoals. Secondly, herring are only noisy at night, so it has been postulated that, rather than fumbling around in the dark, the fish can easily locate one another using their FRTs. Thirdly, the FRTs have the additional benefit of being a safe way for the herring to communicate, as only other herring can hear them – so this method of communication carries no risk of alerting predators to the herring's position.

Another flatulent sea inhabitant is the sand tiger shark, a ferocious-looking fish which has sharp teeth that protrude in all directions, even when the mouth is closed. The shark is denser than water and lacks a swim bladder, so it gulps air into its stomach at the surface of the water, and then lets the air out of its anus, to help itself sink deeper into the water. Gulping air into its stomach also allows the shark to float motionless in the water so that they can seek prey. However, unlike human farts, these specialised emissions aren't produced by gas after eating.

Who was Mike the chicken?

We often use the phrase 'running around like a headless chicken', and it's a well-known fact that when chickens are beheaded they may run around frantically for a time. However, a chicken called Mike lived perfectly well without a head for 18 months after a failed attempt to kill him in 1945. After his head was cut off with an axe, Mike continued to run around and generally live as full a life as a headless chicken might hope for. He preened and pecked with his neck and was fed with ground-up grain and water through an eyedropper.

Mike is believed to have survived so long because much of his spinal cord and brainstem remained intact. He even became a national celebrity, touring the country and being featured in newspaper and magazine articles. However, one tragic night, Mike the chicken choked to death.

In remembrance of Mike's life, the people in Fruita, Colorado, celebrate a yearly event every May called Mike the Headless Chicken's Day. This celebration includes events such as the Run like a Headless Chicken Race, Egg Tossing and Chicken Dance Contest. A website exists in tribute to Mike's memory at www.miketheheadlesschicken.org.

Can it really rain frogs and fishes?

Surprisingly, it is not only frogs and fishes that have been reported to have fallen from the skies, but also showers of snails, maggots, worms, snakes, shellfish and even lizards. There have been thousands of reports from all over the world of showers of either small fish or tiny frogs raining down. However, strangely, nobody has ever seen frogs, fish or other animals being carried up into the skies. The only rational explanation for these bizarre rains is that tornados or water spouts are responsible, as they tend to suck up whatever is in their path and, if the objects are light, take them into the storm clouds. A tornado can carry objects for several miles, before eventually dropping them back to Earth.

Other notable documented events of strange rainfalls include:

- In AD 77, the Roman historian Pliny reported a shower of frogs that fell from the skies. In the fourth century, fish reportedly fell on a town in Greece for three whole days.

- On 24 April 1871, during a heavy thunderstorm, a large number of sticky drops of jelly fell at a railway station at Bath. According to *Symons' Meteorological Magazine* (1871), the egg masses hatched quickly into annelid-like (segmented) worms. A local vicar examined the jelly and watched it turn into some kind of larvae, which he described as 'minute worms in filmy envelopes'. In 1894, another bizarre shower fell on Bath, which was described in *Notes and Queries* (8 September 1894) as consisting of thousands of shilling-sized jellyfish.

- On 15 December 1876, live, dark brown snakes, 30–46cm (12–18in) long, covered the ground after torrential rain on Memphis, Tennessee.

- During a summer storm in 1894 a mass of small frogs rained down on Wigan in Lancashire.

- On 24 June 1911, at Eton, Buckinghamshire, after heavy rainfall the ground was found covered with masses of jelly, the size of peas. Apparently, these lumps of jelly contained numerous eggs, from which larvae soon emerged. It was reported in *Nature* (6 July 1911) that the larvae were of a species of midge.

- During a storm in England in 1939, so many frogs fell from the skies that witnesses were afraid to walk around for fear of squashing them.

- However, perhaps the most disgusting of all these strange events was that which occurred in Bucharest, Romania, on 25 July 1872. On this day, the heat was stifling and the sky cloudless. At around nine o'clock a small cloud appeared on the horizon, and a quarter of an hour afterwards, to the horror of everybody, there was no rain, but small, fat, black worms or grubs covered most of the streets.

Which animal licked leaking fluid from Henry VIII's rotting corpse?

King Henry VIII (1491–1547) ruled England in the sixteenth century. Henry suffered poor health in his later years, and in the late 1520s he began to suffer from leg ulcers that caused him a great deal of discomfort; they may have been the result of varicose veins or an infection of the bone. When they swelled he suffered with pain and dangerous attacks of fever. He is reported to have smelled awful and needed constant medical attention.

Author Robert Hutchinson gives a description of Henry's awful disease, 'He is the personification of geriatric decay. One can almost smell the putrid stench of the rank pus oozing from his ulcers, staining the bandages on his swollen legs. Chapuys [the Spanish ambassador] labelled them, "The worst legs in the world."'

After Henry's death in London in 1547, his huge corpse was put into a large lead coffin and resting on the coffin was a life-like wax effigy of the king dressed in velvet. There was a procession through the streets of London, and the coffin was put down in Syon Chapel – which is where things started to become really unpleasant. One grisly story recalls:

The king, being carried to Windsor to be buried, stood all night among the broken walls of Sion, and there the leaden coffin being cleft by the shaking of the carriage, the pavement of the church was wetted with Henry's blood. In the morning came plumbers to solder the coffin, under whose feet was seen a dog creeping and licking up the king's blood.

Do jackals really feed their offspring with their own vomit?

The jackal, a doglike creature with a bushy tail, is found in many parts of Africa, the Middle East and India. Jackals are members of the dog family and can actually interbreed with both domestic dogs and wolves. Their predators include leopards, hyenas and eagles. The ancient Egyptians believed the jackal-headed god, Anubis, guided the dead to those wise beings who would judge their souls.

Jackals are scavengers that find and eat dead animals in order to survive. They will happily eat decomposing or diseased flesh riddled with maggots, even if it's been rotting for days. When lions and tigers are done with their kills, jackals will happily move in for the revolting leftovers.

Unlike many other animals, jackals mate for life, producing many offspring. After hunting for food, the parents swallow prey they have caught; when they return to the den, the pups lick their faces until they regurgitate the softened food. This rotting, regurgitated mush is then fed to the young!

What is a sea cucumber and why does it eat faeces?

Sea cucumbers are echinoderms, which means that they have spiny skins. There are over 1,000 species of sea cucumber, many of which are, as their name suggests, shaped like soft-bodied cucumbers. All sea cucumbers live in the ocean, either on or in the ocean floor, and they can grow up to 91cm (3ft) long. They move sluggishly over the seabed and often play host to a pencil-thin fish called a pearfish. This fish lives in the sea cucumber's body, and moves in and out of it via its breathing hole, which is also its bumhole.

When confronted by a predator, such as a crab, some sea cucumbers, rather like Spiderman, discharge sticky threads to entangle their enemies – this buys them time to make a hasty escape. Others will violently contract their muscles, causing their internal organs to shoot out of their anus, to scare away the predator.

The sea cucumber's diet consists of faeces and marine snow. The faeces of many animals living in the ocean makes its way to the ocean floor, and marine snow is made up of mucus and small pieces of dead plants, animals and bacteria. Both the faeces and marine snow sink slowly through the ocean depths to the sea floor, where bottom-dwelling scavengers such as worms, clams, sea urchins and sea cucumbers pick up and eat these nutritious foods.

Amazingly, despite the sea cucumber's diet, some cultures consider it to be a delicacy, and an aphrodisiac too – perhaps because the males shoot sperm into the ocean to reproduce. For centuries, the sea cucumber has been highly regarded for its therapeutic and culinary properties by the Chinese.

Why do dogs eat poo?

We all love dogs, don't we? They're so cute, and playful, and affectionate. They wait at the door for you to come home from work and pine when you leave. They'll catch a frisbee or scare off a burglar. They'll guide the blind, sniff out drugs and bombs, and rescue stranded explorers. Dogs are wonderful animals. If only they weren't so, well, disgusting.

For a start, dogs will eat or drink almost anything: stagnant pond water, rubbish, vomit, cat poo, other dogs' poo, even dead maggot-ridden roadkill, and then lick your face. And they seem to be particularly keen on cat poo. Why is this? One reason may be that cat poo is full of things that dogs like and need, such as protein. Protein is needed by animals and humans to keep healthy – fortunately we humans find other ways to get protein, such as by eating meat and cheese.

Other unpleasant canine habits include licking their bums and dragging them across the carpet. The reason they do this may simply be that they are suffering from blocked anal glands, which the licking and chafing may be designed to unblock. A dog's anal sacs are found either side of its anus. They contain a stinky, fishy-smelling liquid that dogs use to mark out their territory. Some poor pooches suffer from trouble with their anal sacs, which can become blocked and irritated. These sacs, when full, are about the size of a marble. Each anal sac has a small tube that opens out to the bumhole. Every time a dog poos, some of this liquid is squirted out at the same time. It gives each dog's poo its own unique odour, which tells other dogs to move their furry butts, because this territory is taken.

Which centipede preys on bats in mid-flight?

Many people are freaked out by insects, especially giant ones, such as the Amazonian giant centipede. This maroon-red centipede has 46 banana-coloured legs, and adults can reach the whopping length of 30cm (12in). These creatures are aggressive, extremely fast runners and excellent climbers.

The giant centipede usually feeds at night, when it creeps out to stalk its unsuspecting targets, which can include birds, lizards, frogs and mice. It gropes through the darkness using its long antennae, before expertly and quickly snagging its prey. It uses its jaws and modified front claws to inject its prey with a powerful and toxic venom. After a quick fight, the quarry dies and the centipede can then tuck into its kill. The giant centipede's venom is highly toxic to humans. It can cause fever, pain, vomiting and severe swelling, and it has even been fatal in some cases.

However, the giant centipede's most extraordinary talent is the one it exhibits while lurking in the dark caves of Venezuela, where it hunts for bats. First the centipede climbs over numerous writhing beetles and then up the wall of the cave; it then scurries across the ceiling into a position near the centre. There, it grips the roof of the cave with its rear legs, allowing the front part of its body to dangle down. As the bats fly through the cave, unaware of the danger, the centipede grabs one from the air in mid-flight. The giant centipede's toxic venom works quickly, and although the bat fights valiantly to get away from its many legs, the struggle proves futile; moments later it succumbs to the venom. While still hanging from the ceiling, the centipede devours its kill.

What is dangerous about the silver carp?

In the 1990s, a type of fish called the silver carp first entered the Mississippi River, after having escaped from a local fish farm following a series of floods. Since that time, the carp have steadily moved upriver and now outnumber local fish by ten to one, and are spreading to other rivers in the area.

One unique danger posed by these fish is the fact that they can leap out of the water; in fact, some have been known to jump 3m (9ft 10in) in a single leap. It seems that one thing that makes them jump is the noise of boat engines, presumably because they think it is a predator chasing them. This makes them especially dangerous from a human point of view, as it means they literally jump with fright at every passing boat. If it were only a handful of fish jumping at any one time, that would be dangerous enough, as they can reach up to 45kg (100lb) in weight – people have described being hit by a silver carp as like being hit by a bowling ball. In fact, they are known to leap in great shoals with as many as 200 leaping out of the water simultaneously, making them an even more serious menace.

There have been numerous reports of large jumping silver carp severely injuring boaters and waterskiers. In June 2004, a woman waterskiing in Illinois was smacked on the head by a massive leaping carp and she suffered concussion. In another case, a fisherman had a big carp suddenly launch itself into his groin. Needless to say, he was in a lot of pain, but thankfully he did make a full recovery.

Which spider carries its babies on its back?

If you take a walk through long grass in the summer, you may notice lots of small spiders scatter from your path. Many of these brown-coloured spiders will be wolf spiders, which are unusual in that they do not make webs to catch their prey. Instead, they hunt, rather like wolves, which is the reason why they are so named. Wolf spiders have excellent vision, with eight big eyes that allow them to be very effective in spotting prey that they then chase down and pounce on. The wolf spider then injects venom into its victim through its powerful fangs, quickly paralysing or killing it. When the prey no longer struggles, the spider injects digestive fluids, which turns its prey's insides into liquid. The victim is then sucked dry of all its nutrients. Wolf spiders hunt small insects and sometimes even other smaller wolf spiders. Worldwide, there are more than 2,000 species of wolf spider, the largest is almost 5cm (2in) long, including the legs.

Rather like a man giving a bunch of flowers to the woman he loves, a male wolf spider may court the larger female by offering her a silk-wrapped dead fly. If successful, he will then transfer his sperm to her via his syringe-like feelers. In other species of wolf spider, when a male spots a female he performs a courtship dance that involves waving his front legs like signal flags and vibrating his abdomen. The female is often not impressed by this showmanship and will react by attacking him. However, if the male persists, the female may allow him to climb on her and mate.

After mating, the female creates an egg sac and attaches it to her abdomen, so that she can carry her eggs around with her. When the many spiderlings have hatched, the female wolf spider will carry them on her back for a week or more. In some species, the brood is so numerous that the spiderlings cover the mother's back several layers deep.

Why should you be wary of a brown recluse?

Worldwide, there are more than 34,000 species of spiders and most of them are venomous. One of the most dangerous spiders in the US is the brown recluse spider; it is also known as the fiddleback spider, brown fiddler, or violin spider on account of a distinctive mark on its back that is in the shape of a violin. One bite from a brown recluse can cause a range of extremely unpleasant symptoms and can even be fatal.

The brown recluse spider is usually between 6mm (¼in) and 20mm (1³⁄₁₆in) long and it ranges in colour from tan to dark brown. Besides the violin marking, it can also be identified by its unusual number of eyes. Most spiders have eight eyes, but the brown recluse has only six, which are arranged in three pairs. The brown recluse is native to the US and is generally found between the southern Midwest states and the Gulf of Mexico. It usually builds its webs in sheds, garages and cellars, and other places which are dry and undisturbed.

As its name suggests, the brown recluse is rather timid. It hides for most of the day but it is active at night and so is more likely to find its way into clothing, bedding and shoes at this time. It would rather run from danger than fight, but if cornered it will bite, and its venom, sphingomyelinase D, is responsible for an array of gruesome symptoms. People rarely see the spider and so they are often unaware that they have been bitten until the symptoms begin. The severity of symptoms depends upon the amount of venom injected and the individual's sensitivity to it. After being bitten some people will experience a stinging sensation in the bite area. Within several hours the individual may suffer with increasing pain and itching. Also, the area may become red, swollen and tender and an unpleasant white blister may form in the centre of the wound.

Most brown recluse bites are fairly minor, but some wounds may become necrotic, which is very nasty indeed.

Necrosis, the root of the word 'necrotic', means the premature death of living cells or tissues as a result of external factors such as injury, toxins or infection. If the wound becomes necrotic, within two to five weeks the spider's venom will start to destroy the tissues at the site of the bite, resulting in a deep, poorly healing ulcer. The spot will grow deeper and larger and may expand up to several inches over a period of weeks. The victim's flesh will become hard and blackened. Other symptoms can include fever, chills, headache, nausea, vomiting, weakness and restlessness. Full recovery can take several months, leaving a nasty scar. Deaths from brown recluse bites are rare, but there have been some among children, the elderly and people with poor health.

Which insects emerge from the ground in their billions every 17 years?

A cicada nymph is a strange-looking insect, with bulging eyes and big hooks on the end of its front legs. It can grow up to 6cm (2½in) in length, which means adult cicadas are among the biggest of all insects. They have two pairs of wings, broad heads and thick, heavy bodies.

The nymphs live underground in total darkness, where they mature over a number of years. During their time underground, they have a ready supply of food as they suck sap from the roots of trees. The *Magicicada septendecium* cicadas live for 17 years underground, and then emerge in their billions in places in the US such as Illinois,

Wisconsin, Michigan and Indiana. Exactly how the cicadas keep track of time while underground has always puzzled researchers. One group of scientists in California has suggested that the nymphs use an external cue that they are able to count. They suggest that when the trees flower, this coincides with a peak in the chemical concentration of the sap that the insects feed on. So, perhaps, the cicadas may tick off the years by counting these peaks.

After their 17 years underground, the cicadas finally emerge. When they reach the surface, they then find the nearest tree to climb and head for the treetops. Once the cicada has climbed a tree, the skin on its back splits and it slowly moves up and out of the slit leaving its exoskeleton behind. Its crumpled wings now pump full of blood and harden, allowing it to fly. Then, at last, the mating season can begin.

When they are mating, the male cicadas make a lot of noise, using a drum-like organ in their body. In fact, they are so loud, the combined noise made by the male cicadas is said to equal 100 decibels. This is louder than a jet aircraft flying overhead and can be heard a quarter of a mile away.

Once the cicadas have mated, the male soon dies. The female lays hundreds of eggs, which she does by making incisions in the bark of a twig and then laying the eggs inside the resulting slit. Once this is done, she also drops dead. The sudden death of all these cicadas leaves a hundred tons of dead and dying carcasses to be cleared up from the area.

After leaving the egg, the cicada nymph emerges from the twig and falls from the tree to the ground. It then begins crawling around, looking for a crack in the ground or some other suitable place to dig where it then hollows out a small chamber around itself. Once the nymph has found a good spot, it will puncture the root of a nearby tree with its sharp beak and begin sucking the tree's sap. This is where it will stay for the next 17 years.

What is monkey-face disease?

Who would think a pretty, delicate white-flowered plant could cause such an unsightly deformity as a lamb born with a single eye in the middle of its forehead? Malformations such as these can result if pregnant ewes eat the poisonous plant *Veratrum californicum*, which is commonly known as false hellebore. It is found on the high mountain ranges of the northern Rockies and in south-western North America.

The most common malformation caused by false hellebore is called monkey-face lamb disease, in which the lamb is born with a deformed head. Usually, the lamb's nose will be shortened, or not be there at all, and its jaw will protrude. It may have an enlarged head and its face may be caved in. In extreme cases, the lamb might even have both eyeballs in one eye socket in the middle of its forehead, creating a cyclopic lamb. Unfortunately, although most livestock generally avoid false hellebore, sheep do not.

Other weird creatures

If you ever find yourself in Paris and have an urge to see a cyclopic head, why not head for the Fragonard Veterinary Museum? There, you will find a wide range of exotic and unusual animal parts on display. At this fascinating museum, not only can you view a cyclopic veal calf's head floating in a jar, but you might also like to observe a cow's ovarian cyst, a horse's tongue or perhaps a skinned cat stretched out like a little rug.

Which insect is the tarantula's worst enemy?

The tarantula spider may seem like a fearsome predator, but it's no match for its worst enemy, a wasp called a tarantula hawk. The tarantula hawk wasp is one of the largest types in the world with a wingspan that reaches 11 cm (4¼in) and a body length of up to 7cm (2¾in). It is found world-wide and is typically metallic blue or black with brightly coloured wings.

When the female wasp picks up the scent of a tarantula, she will hunt it down and then attack it. Strangely, the tarantula rarely retaliates against the wasp and becomes quite docile. Some experts think that the wasp produces chemicals that cause the tarantula to become stupefied. The wasp will then sting the spider, quickly paralysing the arachnid with its neurotoxic venom. The female wasp then lays an egg on the spider's motionless body and pushes it into a burrow. When the hungry baby wasp hatches, it has a ready supply of fresh meat on which to feed. At first, it plunges its mouthparts into the spider's body and feeds on the spider's juices, but as the larva grows quickly, it soon begins eating a diet of solid foods: the spider's organs. All of this happens while the spider is still alive.

What is the fiery serpent?

The fiery serpent is the colloquial name for the guinea worm, which is a very unpleasant parasite that infests humans. The guinea worm is most commonly found among poor communities in remote parts of Africa that do not have access to safe drinking water. It is renowned for causing persistent, excruciating pain and suffering. The worm begins life as a small larva that is swallowed by tiny water fleas in contaminated water.

For humans, the trouble begins when we drink water contaminated with these water fleas. Although gastric acid in the stomach kills the water fleas, it doesn't kill the guinea worm larvae, as they are resistant to this acid. Once released, the larvae then travel along our small intestine and begin their migration. They bore their way out of the intestine, through the intestinal wall, and during the next 10–14 months they grow to adulthood and steadily make their way to our legs. As they make this journey, the worms also mate. After they have mated, the male dies and is absorbed by the female. All this time, they are continuing to grow and they can eventually reach as much as 0.9m (3ft) in length – eventually, they end up looking like a very long strand of spaghetti.

At this point, the adult female steadily moves towards the surface of the skin; usually on the legs, but she may emerge from other areas. As the worm reaches the skin's surface, it creates a blister causing intense, burning pain before finally rupturing within around 24–72 hours. This may also be accompanied by fever, nausea and vomiting.

To relieve the burning pain, many victims will usually try to immerse their leg in cold water, often in a river. However, the temperature change will often cause the skin over the blister to crack, exposing the adult worm and allowing it to release millions of young larvae into the water. At some point, many of these larvae will be eaten by passing water fleas and the whole cycle will begin again. It takes about a year from the time a person drinks infected water for the worm to emerge from the skin.

However, the really unpleasant part of this story concerns the removal of the worm, as there is no drug to treat it. Our natural temptation is to grasp hold of the protruding end of the writhing worm and pull it out. However, this temptation must be resisted, because it could be fatal. If a sufferer tries to rip the worm out and in the process breaks its body, the part of the worm left under the skin will die, releasing large amounts of proteins that cause a sudden, lethal shock.

The only way to remove the worm safely is to prise it out very slowly, a few inches each day. This exceptionally slow, painful process is often done with a small stick about the size and shape of a pencil; it may take a few days to pull it out, although sometimes it can even take weeks. Even once the worm has been successfully removed, people are often left with scarring or are even permanently crippled. Thankfully, this dreadful condition is close to being eradicated, thanks to international efforts to ensure safe drinking water in the poorest parts of the world. According to the World Health Organization, in the 1980s there were more than 3.5 million people infected with guinea worm throughout Africa and Asia. However, in 2008, there were only 4,619 cases, all of which were in Africa.

Which worm can eat its way through the human eye?

There is a parasite called the toxocara worm that is commonly found in dogs and cats. It is the most common parasite in young puppies but causes them no problems. However, the worm can be a problem if transmitted to humans, which can easily occur. The toxocara worm produces a large number of eggs in the stomachs of cats and dogs and these eggs are excreted with the animals' poo. All it then takes is for a person to tread on some dog poo in the street and then transfer the eggs to the carpet back at home or the garden – it's easy to see how a person might become infected.

However, once inside the human, the toxocara worm does not tend to like this environment, so it will try to find its way out. This can result in affected parts of the body becoming inflamed and, although this is rare, the worm may even emerge through the eye, and travel to the brain or the heart. If the worm tries to emerge through the eye, it can ultimately lead to blindness. Treating ocular toxocariasis can be difficult; in some cases, a laser has to be used to kill the worm before it reaches the retina.

Nonetheless, most people who develop toxocariasis recover without needing treatment. Many of them suffer no symptoms at all and never even realise that they had the infection. The good news is that even if symptoms do appear, anti-parasitic medicines can be taken to destroy the worms. About 20 per cent of adult dogs carry toxocara, along with around 80 per cent of puppies. This is why it is so important for dog owners to deworm their pets.

Which wasp lays her eggs inside a cockroach?

The cockroach wasp is around 2cm (¾in) in length and is a myriad of metallic blues and greens. It is native to the Pacific Islands, south-east Asia and parts of Africa. When it finds an unsuspecting cockroach, it will sting it twice. The first sting is designed to paralyse the cockroach but not kill it. This paralysis is only temporary but gives enough time for the wasp to administer its second sting carefully, because this time the sting needs to be much more precise. The second sting delivers venom into the cockroach's brain, affecting its escape reflex, so that when the cockroach comes out of its physical paralysis, it does not feel the need to escape. Instead, it simply grooms itself, giving the wasp time to look for a lair.

When the wasp returns, having found a suitable spot, it bites off one of the cockroach's antennae and laps at the resulting blood. Then, it drags the cockroach around by its other antenna, like a dog on a lead, and takes it back to the nest. Then, she lays an egg on the stupefied cockroach, before burying it, to stop other predators from eating it. The cockroach is still alive, but still has no instinct to escape thanks to the wasp's earlier venomous injection. When the eggs hatch, the wormlike wasp larvae will begin to eat the living flesh of the cockroach. Eventually, after days of voracious eating, the helpless cockroach dies.

How did the death-watch beetle get its name?

The death-watch beetle is a small, wood-boring beetle that is about 7mm (5/16in) long. The male death-watch beetle attracts a female by knocking his head against the wooden beams of the old building in which the female lives. She, in turn, answers by banging with her head.

For centuries people were terrified by the sound of the death-watch beetle. In olden days, when people heard the ominous 'tap, tap, tap' sounds, they thought it meant that someone in the house was going to die, which is how the beetle got its name. Many writers have made use of the death-watch beetle's ominous, atmospheric quality. For example, in Edgar Allan Poe's sinister story The *Tell-Tale Heart*, the unnamed narrator hears the death-watch beetle tapping in the walls, while he watches his victim in his bedchamber.

What are the world's scariest creatures?

As is probably becoming clear, the natural world is full of disgusting, vile, nauseating creatures, but which is the most sickening? One contender must be the world's largest crab: the Japanese spider crab. Although its body only measures around 30cm (12in) across, its outstretched leg span reaches over 3.5m (11ft 6in)! It can be found in the northern Pacific Ocean, where it lives in deep water and thankfully never surfaces. It is adapted to withstand great water pressure at depths of 1,000m (3,300ft) or more.

Another intimidating sea dweller is the colossal squid, which can grow up to 12m (40ft) in length, and could easily play a starring role in a horror film. It has huge, rotating hooks that grow from its suckers, an extremely large, sharp beak and enormous pop eyes that are the largest eye of any animal – the size of a dinner plate. In 2003, fishermen in the Ross Sea off Antarctica became the first people ever to see a colossal squid alive. It was feeding on fish caught on their fishing lines. It was almost 6m (20ft) long, about half its full, adult size.

Africa's goliath beetle is one of the biggest and heaviest insects in the world and can be found in tropical regions of Africa and also in the Amazon rainforest. They are as big as a human fist and measure about 15cm (6in) long and 6cm (2½in) across, and their primary food source is faeces. They are good fliers and make the sound of a low, helicopter-like whirring while flying. Sometimes, African children like to tie the beetles on to lengths of string and watch them fly around in circles. Male goliath beetles have a horn-shaped structure on their heads that they use to fight with other goliath beetles.

Why do insects fall prey to pitcher plants?

Around the world, there are more than 600 different species of carnivorous plants. One group of these are called pitcher plants, of which the two main families are the Nepenthaceae and Sarraceniaceae. Pitcher plants are commonly found in the US, and they come in an array of colours including yellow, green, red and white; some can grow as high as 1.2m (4ft) tall.

All pitcher plants work by catching their prey in an unusually shaped, hollow leaf structure, which looks like a pitcher or a jug. First, the plant has to attract the insects. To do this, pitcher plants have a lid or hood over the pitcher that contains nectar. This lid also serves to prevent the pitcher from filling with rainwater. Once the insect is inside, hairs within the lid direct the insect deeper into the plant. As it explores further, the insect will suddenly reach a smooth, waxy area, found on the upper part of the pitcher, which causes it to slide into the liquid below and drown. The insect is unable to climb out of the pitcher, because the hairs inside it grow downward and act as spears, blocking its path. The liquid the insect falls into contains acids and enzymes to help digest food. When the insect falls into this liquid, its soft body parts will slowly dissolve in these digestive juices. Fungi and bacteria are also found inside pitcher plants, which also help to break down the insects' bodies.

The yellow pitcher plant, also known as the trumpet pitcher plant because of its trumpet-shaped leaves, ensures its insect victims cannot escape by lacing its nectar with coniine. This drug is a narcotic to insects, and it paralyses them. The insect then falls into the trumpet pitcher's liquid and is digested. As rotting insect bodies fill the plant, the smell attracts other potential victims: blowflies. This plant is so effective at catching prey that it may contain as many as a thousand insects; so many, in fact, that the plant can become too heavy and topple over. Sometimes, even frogs have become prey, after slipping into the plant while hunting insects.

However, there are some insects that do not fall victim to the pitcher plant, but instead use it as a source of food. Some spiders make webs across the pitcher's leaf opening, so that when insects fly in to drink nectar, they become caught in the web, providing the spider with a meal. Some mosquitoes and flies lay their eggs in the pitcher's liquid. These eggs are unaffected by the plant's digestive juices, and when they hatch, the larvae find themselves surrounded by rotting insect parts on which to feast.

Although the main diet of pitcher plants is typically bugs and insects, there is one variety which sometimes preys on even larger creatures. The tropical pitcher plant, which is found mainly in the rainforests of south-east Asia, contains some pitchers as large as footballs – it has been known to devour whole birds, frogs and even rats.

CHAPTER THREE

Vile bodies

What did Queen Victoria see floating in the river Cam?

Today, the river Cam in Cambridgeshire is one of the most picturesque of English rivers. However, back in the 1800s, it wasn't an idyllic place to sit beside and eat a picnic, as it was rather smelly. All of Cambridge's sewage flowed into it, making it simply a large open sewer and a pretty disgusting place to be near.

In 1843, Queen Victoria (1819–1901) was walking beside the river with her companion, a university lecturer called Dr Whewell, and as they crossed the bridge, the queen looked down into the water and asked, 'What are all those pieces of paper floating down the river?' They were actually bits of poo-covered toilet paper, but the quick-thinking lecturer replied, 'Those, ma'am, are notices warning that bathing is forbidden.'

How did Napoleon's haemorrhoids affect the outcome of the battle of Waterloo?

Napoleon Bonaparte (1769–1821) was born in Corsica. He became a general in the French army in 1796, and after staging a successful coup in 1799, he crowned himself Emperor of France in 1804. Napoleon is considered one of the greatest military commanders of all time, and until 1815 he never lost a battle at which he was present on the field. However, in 1815 Napoleon was defeated, at Waterloo in what is now Belgium, by the British and Prussian troops under the command of the Duke of Wellington and General Marshal Blücher. But how could haemorrhoids have played a part in this defeat?

Napoleon suffered from both constipation and very painful haemorrhoids, which are itchy, swollen veins in the region of the anus. Historians say that, before every battle, Napoleon would survey the battlefield on horseback. However, before the battle of Waterloo, he was suffering from a particularly painful and severe case of haemorrhoids, which prevented him from being able to mount his horse, as it caused him severe physical comfort. Maybe if he had been able to inspect the battlefield, he may have won the battle.

There is also a theory that Napoleon suffered from scabies. Many famous paintings of Napoleon show him with his hand in his shirt; this may have been a fashionable pose at the time, or perhaps he simply had an itch that needed scratching? Scabies is a parasitic infestation of tiny mites that burrow under the skin, leaving behind a trail of white and black dots, which are their eggs and poo respectively, and they cause intense itching. Napoleon was often to be found soaking in hot baths, sometimes several times a day. If a person did have scabies, they might take regular hot baths to soothe their inflamed, itchy skin.

During the Russian campaign, Napoleon's troops were thought to have been widely infected with scabies, and Napoleon is thought to have transmitted them to his wife, Josephine. Napoleon's doctor was the Frenchman Corvisart, who is considered to have been one of the most brilliant physicians of the early nineteenth century. Corvisart was apparently able to cure Napoleon of scabies by prescribing a mixture containing alcohol, olive oil and powdered cevadilla (derived from a tropical lily that grows in Mexico and Central America), which was applied to the skin.

Why would a man volunteer to be castrated?

Many readers may wince to learn that down the years there have been many examples of men volunteering for castration. Some have done so out of religious piety. George Rapp, for example, was one of the most famous castrates of the nineteenth century. Rapp founded the Harmony Society of Utopian Christians, in Pennsylvania. He believed that sex was immoral, and he strongly urged his community to live in celibacy. To demonstrate his devotion, Rapp took the extraordinary step of castrating himself, and he was also accused of castrating his son and several other men.

Castration was not uncommon in the early 1800s, as it was often prescribed in the treatment of mumps and other diseases.

What underwear blocks the smell of farts?

Let's face it, everyone farts, and studies have shown that when men and women eat the same food, women produce more concentrated gas then men; in other words, stinkier farts! Farts are caused by the food we've eaten and the air we've ingested.

However, there are some medical conditions known to cause flatulence too. For example, Arlene Weimer of Pueblo, Colorado, suffers from a condition called Crohn's disease that causes symptoms including inflammation of the digestive tract, diarrhoea and flatulence. Luckily, Arlene's husband Buck is an inventive type, who decided to take action. In an article featured in the *Denver Post* in 2001, Buck said, 'I'm laying in bed with her, sort of suffering silently, and out of the silence came determination. Something had to be done.' He set to work to try to come up with a solution to the problem of his wife's flatulence.

Buck had the idea of using a filter, but he realised that it couldn't be too big and bulky, and, of course, it would have to absorb any bad smells. He experimented with the filters used in the gas masks worn by coal miners. He put one into his pants, and although it didn't work perfectly, he knew he was on the right track. He carried on working on prototypes until, six years later, he came up with his brand new invention: Under-Ease. This airtight underwear has a replaceable charcoal filter that removes bad-smelling gases before they can escape. In this way, the pants are supposed to hide the smell of farts completely by preventing the noxious gas from escaping. Unfortunately, they don't prevent the 'parp' noise which accompanies the trumping. Naturally anxious that no one should steal his revolutionary new idea, Buck registered a patent in 1998.

Buck's Under-Ease pants are made from a soft, airtight, nylon-type fabric, with elastic around the waist and legs. The removable filter, which looks a bit like a shoulder pad, is made of charcoal sandwiched between two layers of Australian sheep's wool. Buck explains how the filter mechanism works:

> The multi-layered filter pad traps the 1–2 per cent of human gas creating the foul smell (mostly hydrogen sulphide), but allows the remaining non-smelling gas to pass through. It also allows the natural build-up of body heat to pass through. They can be worn anytime, anywhere – to work, social events, professional meetings, even on an aeroplane. And thankfully, the pants are machine washable.

The company's motto is 'wear them for the ones you love'.

What is a love bug?

If you're suffering with intense, persistent itching in the genital area, there's a good chance you could be suffering from love bugs, also known as pubic lice or crab lice. The French have a much nicer term for these little pests, giving them the rather poetic name of *papillons d'amour*, which literally means 'butterflies of love'.

Pubic lice are usually transmitted during close physical contact with an infected individual. The lice may be seen moving around in the pubic hair, and they are particularly active at night, which causes intense itching. They are well adapted to live in pubic, underarm, beard and eyelash hair, which can become quite unsightly when peppered with lice eggs. However, the pubic louse strikes gold when it finds an extremely hairy man, as a hirsute host will provide it with a wide expanse to frolic around in and lay eggs

The crab louse is so named because of its shape and powerful claws that resemble a crab's pincers. It uses these claws to grasp our hair, and it can live for up to 30 days in the pubic hair. Female crab lice stick their eggs to hair shafts using a cement-like substance. The good news is that there is an effective treatment that can be applied to the affected area, which will cure this itchy affliction.

What was the Great House of Easement?

In the early Tudor era, there were no flushing toilets. Instead, Henry VIII rested the royal posterior on a close stool.

It consisted of a bucket and water tank, with a padded seat lavishly covered in black velvet.

However, Henry's courtiers used the malodorous communal facilities of the House of Easement at Hampton Court, a two-storey facility that consisted of rows of oak seats, with holes cut in the wood at two-foot intervals. Chutes made of bricks or stone would carry the waste down to a basin that then flowed directly into the river Thames. However, some of the more solid waste would collect in the brick chambers, which had to be cleaned regularly. This stinky task was given to gong scourers, who were also known as gongfermors or gong farmers. The gong scourers were often young boys, as it was their misfortune to be small enough to crawl along the drains.

Is it true that Ivan the Terrible would often bang his head on the floor until it was bruised and bloody?

Ivan the Terrible (1530–84) became the ruler of Russia at the age of three, following his father's death. After his mother was murdered by poisoning, the rich noblemen known as the boyars took over the leadership of the country. Murders and beatings were regular events at the palace and the boyars killed four of Ivan's uncles and other important personages at the court – these killings were often witnessed by Ivan. While Ivan was young, the nobles treated him very cruelly – he was neglected, dressed in rags, beaten and tortured. He took his frustrations out on animals and enjoyed pulling out the feathers of live birds, piercing their eyes and cutting open their bodies. As he grew older, he took his frustrations out on people and became cruel and vindictive. When he was 15, Ivan was offended by a nobleman who was apparently rude to him, so he ordered the man's tongue to be cut out. Ivan suffered with paranoia and had a vicious temper, and it was said that when he became angry, he would foam at the mouth like a horse.

Despite his shocking brutality, Ivan nonetheless considered himself to be a deeply religious man. He would often go to church when he had sinned, pray for forgiveness, and then bang his head on the floor before the altar. He did this so much he would leave the church with his head bleeding and bruised, and claim he was now cleansed.

Ivan appointed military officers known as *oprichniki*. They wore black uniforms and carried a dog's head on their horse's bridle and a brush fastened to their whip. These items symbolised the hunting down of Ivan's enemies and then sweeping them away. Some examples of Ivan's cruelty are:

- In 1547, 75 citizens of Pskov complained against the governor of the town. This enraged Ivan so much that he made them undress and lie on the floor, with their hands tied behind their backs. As they lay prostrate, boiling wine was poured onto their heads, and their hair and beards were also set alight.

- Ivan and his oprichniki attacked the city of Novgorod, in 1570, as he was angry that the city did not submit abjectly to his authority. For five weeks they tortured, raped and murdered up to 60,000 people. It is said that so much blood entered the city's river that it didn't freeze over in winter for years afterwards.

- Later, in 1575, Archbishop Leonid of Novgorod was accused of a whole array of crimes including treason, buggery, bestiality and keeping witches. Leonid's large fortune was confiscated by Ivan, 11 of his servants were hanged and his 'women witches' were dismembered and burnt. Legend has it that Ivan ordered Leonid to be sewn into a bear's skin, and he then ordered it to be thrown to a pack of hungry dogs. In the same year, there was a famine, and Ivan invited some starving peasants to dinner. Instead of feeding them, he murdered them and threw them into the river.

What were 'Waterloo teeth'?

At the battle of Waterloo in 1815, such was the scale of loss of life that there were rich pickings for the British troops when the battle was over. The dead were stripped of any-thing of value, including their teeth. Such a vast number of teeth were extracted from the dead at Waterloo that for many years afterwards dentures were known as 'Waterloo teeth'. A tooth transplant involved taking a tooth from one person and transplanting it into the head of another person, and many people unwittingly wore teeth extracted from the soldiers.

Tooth transplants plummeted in popularity when it was discovered that infections such as syphilis could be transmitted in this way.

Have people ever been allowed to expose their private parts in public?

These days, it would be a definite fashion faux pas to go out wearing clothing that exposed one genitals. However, this wasn't always the case. Back in the 1300s, men wore a kind of tights called hose. Hose consisted of two separate stockings, tailored from cloth, which would be laced onto the bottom of the wearer's tunic. As the hose only covered the legs and men didn't wear underwear, this left a gap between the legs. This was fine as long as tunics were of a decent length, but, over time, a fashion developed for tunics to get shorter and shorter. Eventually, the tunics became so short that they didn't adequately cover a man's groin, often leaving his private parts on view.

In 1482, King Edward IV (1442–83) passed a law that men had to cover their genitals, and as a result codpieces quickly became very fashionable. Originally, the codpiece was a triangular flap in the hose that served the function of a modern trouser fly: it could be unbuttoned or untied to allow the wearer to urinate. However, over time, the codpiece became larger to help accentuate a man's private parts, with some codpieces protruding as much as 13cm (5in).

Author Michel de Montaigne (1533–92) was not a fan of the codpiece and sniffed, 'What is the purpose of that monstrosity that we to this day have fixed to our trousers, and often which is worse, it is beyond its natural size through falseness and imposture?' Men were often accused of stuffing them to exaggerate the size of their genitals.

By the 1500s, codpieces were heavily padded, so that they stuck out from the rest of the clothes, and they were decorated with ribbons, puffs and jewelled pins. However, by the 1590s, codpieces had become passé.

Where can you find a place called Bollock?

Throughout UK, there are numerous places with rude and saucy connotations, including Grope Lane, Juggs Close, Crapstone, Crotch Crescent, Slutshole Lane and Titty Ho. Scratchy Bottom can be found in Dorset, while there is a Lickey End in Worcestershire. However, smutty place names are not confined to the UK. The following is a list of some of the more outlandish place names from around the world:

- Bastard – Norway
- Bollock – Philippines
- Bumbang – Australia
- Chinaman's Knob – Australia
- Condom – France
- Crap – Albania
- Dikshit – India
- Dildo – Newfoundland
- Fucking – Austria
- Knob Lick – Missouri
- Labia – Belgium
- Minge – Lithuania
- Semen – Bulgaria
- Shag Island – Indian Ocean
- Shit – Iran
- Slut – Sweden
- Turda – Romania
- Vagina – Russia
- Wank – Germany

Did Hitler really suffer with flatulence?

Adolf Hitler (1889–1945) was well known for being a hypochondriac and suffered from uncontrollable farting, according to biographer John Tolan. Hitler told a doctor in the early 1930s, 'The cramps are so severe that sometimes I could scream out loud!' However, a Berlin doctor called Theodor Morell prescribed Dr Koester's Anti-Gas Pills, which Hitler took for many years. However, although they apparently succeeded in reducing the flatulence, it seems the pills would have done him more harm than good, as they contained strychnine and belladonna, which are two deadly poisons. According to Alan Bullock, in his biography of Hitler, the poisons accounted for the Führer's ash-grey skin colouring and shaking limbs towards the end of his life. Severe periodontal gum disease also caused him to suffer with halitosis (foul-smelling breath).

Which disease caused its victims' organs to liquefy?

The Black Death or bubonic plague (1348–50) was the most virulent plague that history has ever recorded. Its name came from the black swellings that were found on many of its victims; other symptoms included pain, fever and vomiting blood. The plague caused internal bleeding, and in the final days, the victims' vital organs began turning to liquid and rotting away. Mercifully, death would come soon after. Once a person contracted the plague, recovery was rare, although a few people did survive the disease.

The Black Death was responsible for killing up to half the population of Europe and struck England in 1348. It was at its worst in cities, where there was enormous over-crowding, and poor hygiene and sanitation. When the plague reached London, in 1348, up to 30,000 people died – nearly half the city's population. Over the period of the Black Death, the population of England halved from around six million to three million. So many perished that the graveyards were soon full and corpses had to be buried in fields.

Plague epidemics occurred regularly across Europe following the Black Death. The last outbreak of plague in England was the Great Plague of 1665. As in 1348, the plague spread quickly and killed many people. The plague's victims developed painful pus-filled swellings, or buboes, in their groins and armpits. The buboes were red at first, but later turned a dark purple or black.

When spots caused by blood seeping from damaged

blood vessels beneath the skin were found on the body, this was the death certificate for almost all sufferers. The pain was so unbearable that some victims threw themselves out of windows. Sufferers also experienced an unquenchable thirst which led to some of them running naked through the streets, screaming and plunging themselves into water tanks.

To help ensure that victims did not pass on the infection, they were forced to stay in their houses, and the doors were nailed shut and marked with a large red cross. Searchers were paid to remove corpses of victims from homes, and they walked around streets calling, 'Bring out your dead.' As more people became sick the rich left the city, and most of the doctors and clergy went with them. The poor, on the other hand, were not allowed to leave, as they were seen as the carriers of the disease and could infect others.

The famous London diarist Samuel Pepys (1633–1703) kept a diary throughout the Great Plague. In it, on 7 June he recorded the main events in London in the scorching hot summer of 1665:

> The hottest day that I have ever felt in my life. In Drury Lane I saw two or three houses were marked with a red cross and the words 'Lord have mercy upon us' written on the door. This worried me so much that I bought a roll of tobacco to smell and chew.

At the time of the Great Plague, nobody knew the cause of the infection. Some people believed that poisonous air spread the disease, while others blamed cats and dogs; as a result, many thousands were destroyed. On 31 August Samuel Pepys entered the following into his diary:

> Fires were lit to keep the air clean … All dogs and cats are to be caught and killed. People are being paid to kill them. Even public entertainment has been stopped, there's no theatre, no sports and no games. Any houses containing plague victims have to be sealed for 40 days.

The Great Plague claimed around 100,000 victims, but by wintertime it had gone.

Experts believe that it was caused by a bacterium called *Yersina pestis* that lived inside fleas. These fleas were carried by black rats, and when the flea bit a person, it would transfer the bacteria, resulting in the victim contracting the plague. Historians think that plague-carrying rats and fleas were brought to England on boats from Europe. However, some experts take a different view. They argue that because the Black Death spread so quickly, it must have been caused by a virus that can be passed from person to person, like the disease Ebola fever, which also causes massive internal bleeding.

Where can you find the Mound of Ears?

Toyotomi Hideyoshi (1535–98) was the ruler of Japan in the late 1500s. He was a son of a peasant, and he began as a foot soldier in service of his lord Oda Nobunaga. His exceptional military talents ensured that he quickly climbed through the ranks to become Nobunaga's premier general. However, Nobunaga was assassinated in 1582, and so Hideyoshi became the ruler of Japan. In the 1500s, Japan was made up of principalities that were almost constantly at war with each other. Both Nobunaga and Hideyoshi helped to unify the country. Hideyoshi had visions of conquering China via Korea, and in the 1590s Hideyoshi and his troops invaded Korea.

There, Hideyoshi and his men hacked off tens of thousands of Koreans' heads, including those of women and children. The taking of heads in battle was an age-old practice in east Asia. The victorious armies would take the severed heads of their defeated enemy and present them to their commander as a proof of victory. Hideyoshi wanted to ship the heads back to Japan, but it proved too impractical, as the heads took up too much room, as well as no doubt being extremely smelly and unpleasant. Instead he decided to just send back the ears and noses in barrels of salt water to preserve them. The trophies were systematically recorded against each individual warrior's name and shipped back to Japan, where a mound of them was created – it is now called the Mound of Ears (*Mimizuka*). The 9m (30ft)-high war memorial can still be seen in Kyoto.

What was the unpleasant job of a *decrotteur*?

In the 1700s, Paris was the world's cultural hub; it was the centre of science, art, fashion – generally a city of exquisite taste. Nonetheless, it was also, according to Louis Sebastien Mercier, a French playwright of the time, 'the centre of stench'. In a memorable account, Mercier described a main street in Paris as being 'covered with stagnant water and dead cats'.

According to Jean-Jacques Rousseau, the eighteenth-century French philosopher, in the courthouse, in the museum, at the opera, even at the palace of Versailles, 'one does not know where to sit in summer, without inhaling the odour of stagnant urine'. Courtyards, corridors and alleys would be full of urine and faeces. In addition, urine and faeces were thrown from chamber pots being emptied out of windows, and these often landed onto the heads of people passing by; the person throwing the excreta would call out, '*Garde l'eau!*', which meant literally, 'Look out for the water!' Over time, the streets became choked with excrement. Carriages tearing down the streets would throw up the sludge, splashing pedestrians with rubbish and raw sewage.

So what was a person to do if attending some sophisti-cated event at which an outfit matted with excrement might be regarded as a somewhat outré? Luckily, Parisian high society catered for just this problem; the grand houses would employ a person called a *decrotteur*, which literally meant a de-shitter. It was the *decrotteur*'s rather unglam-orous responsibility to wait at the door and clean the shoes and stockings of new arrivals, so that they might enter polite society in as respectable and dignified a manner as possible.

In which society do men tie their penis into a knot?

Warriors of the Karamojong tribe in northern Uganda believe that possession of a very long penis is a wondrous thing. To achieve a suitably impressive member, they tie weights to the end of their penis – a process which begins when a boy reaches puberty. Over time, the amount of weight attached is steadily increased; this can result in a penis reaching as much as 46cm (18in) in length. However, all this process achieves is to stretch the penis, so although it does become longer there is a commensurate decrease in girth with the penis becoming extremely thin. And since a very long, thin penis can get in the way of everyday chores, the tribesmen will often tie it into a knot or two when not in use.

In South African Bantu groups, elongated labia are regarded as a sign of great beauty, so the women of this society will go to great lengths to ensure, well, a great length! They achieve this by regular tugging of the labia minora. There is a similar tradition in southern Tanzania, where the traditional Masai women elongate their labia through massage.

Where might you see a penis 1.7m (5ft 7in) long?

The Icelandic Phallological Museum was founded by teacher and writer Sigurdur Hjartarson and boasts over 260 penises. Hjartarson began collecting penises as a hobby in 1974, and he explains his strange hobby by simply stating, 'I wasn't interested in collecting stamps.' So when someone kindly gave him a bull's penis many years ago, which apparently resembled a riding crop, he decided that he would become a collector of penises.

Since then he hasn't looked back, and his museum proudly displays penises of all shapes and sizes, ranging from the enormous 1.7m (5ft 7in) specimen of a sperm whale, to a 2mm (1⁄16in) hamster penis bone, which really needs to be observed with the help of a magnifying glass. Most of the museum's penises have been donated, but Hjartarson has had to pay for some exhibits, including the elephant penis, which is nearly 1m (3ft 4in) long and is stuffed and mounted on a wooden board. Other exhibits include the penises of skunks, wallabies and bears, which are, depending on their size, displayed either in special tanks or humble glass jars. Surprisingly perhaps, the museum, at present, does not include a human penis in its collection. However, Hjartarson is confident that this shortcoming will soon be rectified, as cocksure men from all parts of the world have generously volunteered to donate their penis after their death.

How does Disney's *Snow White* differ from the original gruesome tale?

Walt Disney's film *Snow White and the Seven Dwarfs* (1937) is an enchanting tale about a beautiful young princess, who is forced to work in rags as a maid for her jealous stepmother, the wicked queen. When a young prince shows interest in Snow White, the queen commands one of her huntsmen to kill the beautiful princess. However, as the huntsman is fond of Snow White, he doesn't kill her and she is consequently looked after by seven dwarfs. After being poisoned by the queen, Snow White is reawakened by the kiss of a prince.

However, in the original story by the Brothers Grimm, there's quite a bit more gore. The Brothers Grimm were two German brothers, Jacob and Wilhelm, who were famous for collecting folk tales such as Sleeping Beauty, Snow White, and Hansel and Gretel, and publishing them in the 1800s.

In the Grimms' *Snow White*, the queen orders the huntsman to bring her the heart and the tongue of Snow White. The huntsman takes Snow White to the forest, draws his knife, and when he is about to pierce her heart, she begins to weep and begs for her life. The huntsman kills a boar instead, and he gives the queen the boar's heart and tongue. She eats these, believing they belong to Snow White. At the end, when Snow White is revived and marries the prince, the evil queen attends the wedding. She is surprised when a pair of shoes made of iron are brought out, flaming hot from the oven. The wicked queen is forced to put them on, and she has to dance until she falls down dead.

Who carried around Walter Raleigh's head for nearly 30 years?

It is well known that the celebrated English adventurer Sir Walter Raleigh (1552–1618) was a key figure in popularising tobacco-smoking in Britain. During the 1500s, tobacco was seldom used for pleasure but was seen as a cure-all to treat almost every illness imaginable. Everything from skin complaints to gangrenous limbs were treated with tobacco, which was mostly taken as snuff. After taking up pipe-smoking Walter began to promote and sell tobacco to the rich. The upper classes embraced the habit of pipe-smoking, and soon tobacco could be purchased in pubs and shops. Its popularity made Walter a lot of money.

James VI of Scotland not only disliked smoking, but also hated Raleigh. When he became King of England in 1603, following the death of Elizabeth I, James had Raleigh, who was a Protestant, arrested and tried as a conspirator in a planned Catholic uprising. Raleigh was found guilty, even though the evidence was flimsy at best, and he was later sentenced to death.

Raleigh was beheaded in 1618 at the age of 66, and his body was buried in St Margaret's church, next to Westminster Abbey. However, his head was put into a red leather bag and given to his widow, Elizabeth. She had Walter's head embalmed, and is said to have carried it around with her wherever she went. Apparently, when people came to visit her at home, she would ask them if they'd like to see Walter. If they agreed, she would bring his head out of the bag. She continued carrying it around right up to her death 29 years later. But that was not the end of the story because, even after Elizabeth's death, her son Carew continued the tradition, carrying his father's head with him everywhere he went. When Carew eventually died in 1666, his father's head was buried with him in West Horsley, Surrey.

CHAPTER FOUR

Pernicious practices

For what unusual purpose did Hippocrates recommend the use of pigeon droppings?

Hippocrates (460–377 BC) was an ancient Greek physician, who is widely regarded as the father of medicine and the founder of a more modern, scientific approach to illness that rejected superstition and divine influence. One of Hippocrates' more unusual recommendations was that bald men should apply pigeon droppings to their bald spot to encourage the hair to regrow. This may sound bizarre, but it is just one of many crazy cures for baldness that have been suggested since the earliest times, as, throughout history, bald men have tried just about anything to stimulate hair growth. The ancient Egyptians, for example, recommended the application of rotten crocodile or hippo fat, thinking that the bad smell would stimulate growth.

Ancient Romans had an ingenious use for houseflies. They thought that if they mashed them up into a paste, which was then applied onto a bald spot, the hair would grow back. Julius Caesar was said to have been follicularly challenged, so Cleopatra applied a substance containing ground horse teeth and deer marrow to his bald spots.

And the wacky remedies didn't die out with the ancient world. Even as recently as Victorian times, desperate slap-heads were applying chicken faeces to their bald spots and encouraging cows to lick their heads.

Who has the world's longest ear hair?

According to the *Guinness Book of World Records*, the person with the world's longest ear hair is Anthony Victor, who lives in India. At its longest, Mr Victor's ear hair measures an incredible 18.1cm (7in).

Other revolting and unusual records include:

- The longest leg hair belongs to Wesley Pemberton, who lives in the US; it measures 16.51cm (6½in) long. It was measured on the set of *Lo Show dei Record*, in Madrid, Spain, in 2008.

- The record for the world's loudest burp belongs to Paul Hunn, who lives in the UK. Hunn set his record in 2000 by letting out an ear-splitting burp of 118.1 decibels – the noise equivalent to a jet engine at take-off.

- Kim Goodman of the US can pop her eyeballs to a pro-trusion of 12mm (½in) beyond her eye sockets. This astonishing feat was measured in Istanbul, Turkey, in 2007.

- In 2001, Ken Edwards, who lives in the UK, set a record in London by eating 36 cockroaches in one minute. He said eating them was like 'having an anaesthetic at the back of the throat'.

- The world's longest tongue belongs to Stephen Taylor of the UK, whose prominent protuberance measures 9.5cm (3⅝in) from its tip to the centre of his closed top lip. It was measured on the set of *Lo Show dei Record* in Milan, Italy, in 2006.

- Until recently, the longest fingernails in the world belonged to a lady named Lee Redmond of the US, who had not cut her nails since 1979. She had a total nail length of 8.65m (28ft 4½in), as measured on the set of *Lo Show dei Record* in Madrid, Spain, in 2008. The longest nail was the right thumb, which was 90cm (2ft 11in) long. However, in February 2009 Redmond was involved in a car crash in which her nails were damaged beyond repair.

- According to *The Illustrated Book of Sexual Records*, one woman had pubic hair that reached down to her knees. The remarkably hirsute Maoni Vi of Cape Town, South Africa, had pubic hair which measured 71cm (2ft 4in) from her groin, while the hair from her armpits measured an amazing 81cm (2ft 8in).

What is the Schmidt Sting Pain Index?

If you've ever suffered the pain of a bee or wasp sting, it can be hard imagine why someone would encourage insects to sting them. However, one brave entomologist decided to allow a variety of insects to inflict stings on his body, all in the name of science.

In the 1980s, biologist Justin O. Schmidt of the South-western Biological Institute in Tucson, Arizona, devised a scale of insect stings according to how much they hurt. The Schmidt Sting Pain Index is not a scientific scale, but it does give us some idea of which insects have the most painful stings. The index starts from a '0', which is the sensation of being stung by an insect that cannot penetrate human skin, progressing up to a '4', for the most painful stings.

According to Schmidt, the most painful sings come from tarantula hawk wasps, bullet ants and velvet ants. He described the tarantula hawk sting as being 'blinding, fierce, shockingly electric. A running hair drier has been dropped into your bubble bath. If you get stung by one, you might as well lie down and scream.' Apparently, the only insect with a worse sting is the bullet ant, a terrifying insect from the Amazon rainforest, whose sting Schmidt describes as 'pure, intense, brilliant pain. Like walking over flaming charcoal with a three-inch nail in your heel.'

Which billionaire had six-inch-long toenails?

Billionaire Howard Hughes (1905–76) inherited a fortune from his father, who was an inventor and manufacturer of oil-mining equipment and tools in Houston, Texas. By the time Howard was 18 both his parents had died, leaving him devastated. At 21, he became the legal owner of all the Hughes businesses.

However, Howard was not content to simply carry on the family business. Instead, he set his heart on success in Hollywood. In 1927, he produced his first movie, *Everybody's Acting*, which was followed the next year by *Two Arabian Nights*. Both were financial successes, with the latter film also winning the Academy Award for Best Director of a Comedy Picture. As Hughes went from success to success in Hollywood, he was simultaneously making a name for himself as a pioneering aviator. Hughes set multiple world air-speed records; in 1938, he completed a flight around the world in just three days and 19 hours. He was also a notorious playboy, who was linked with many of the most desirable women of the age, including Ava Gardner, Katherine Hepburn and Bette Davis.

However, today Howard Hughes is mostly remembered for his bizarre behaviour in his later life. He developed an incapacitating obsessive compulsive disorder (OCD) and lived in fear of germs. One of his aides, Bob Roberts, described the old man sitting in a chair, staring at the wall. Hughes was naked except for a napkin spread over his groin. His long hair was white and dirty, and his toenails and fingernails were some 15cm (6in) long – his toenails were so long that they made a clicking sound when he wiggled his toes. Hughes's doctor wasn't allowed to touch him or speak to him, so they communicated by writing and exchanging notes. Reluctance to part with his faeces caused Hughes to suffer with constipation, which was probably the cause of his bad case of haemorrhoids. It would have been particularly painful when wiping his bottom, considering his six-inch-long fingernails.

His obsession with hidden germs that could potentially cause him harm meant that he avoided contact with possible sources of dirt, and he was constantly washing his hands. He also kept his curtains permanently closed and his windows and doors sealed with masking tape. He was concerned about germs in his carpet, so he walked around with tissue boxes on his feet. Hughes also insisted that his urine should not be flushed down the toilet, but stored in jars instead; and he also stopped taking baths.

For the last 15 years or so of his life, Hughes never left his bedroom. Many hours were spent watching movies, while lying naked on dirty sheets. Ironically, by lying in filth, believing that the outside world was too dirty, Hughes greatly increased his chances of catching the hepatitis that he was so anxious to avoid.

Could cat ear mites live inside a human ear?

In a series of gross and bizarre experiments, a curious New York veterinarian named Dr Robert Lopez attempted to determine whether *Otodectes cynotis*, an ear mite usually found in cats and dogs, could also infest human beings. Lopez later described the study in an article entitled 'Of Mites and Man' for the 1993 *Journal of the American Veterinary Medical Association*. Lopez explained how the study came about:

> A client, accompanied by her three-year-old daughter, brought in two cats with severe ear mite infestations. In the examining room, the daughter happened to complain of an itching chest and abdomen. The mother stated that the daughter frequently held the cats for long periods, like dolls … After the cat's ear mite infestation was cleared up, I learned that the daughter's itching quickly disappeared. At that time (1968), a search of the literature did not reveal any report of *Otodectes cynotis* infestation in human beings, so I decided to be a guinea pig.

He began his experiment by transferring ear mites from a cat. Firstly, he moistened a sterile, cotton-tipped swab and transferred approximately 1g of ear mites from the cat to his left ear. Immediately, he began to hear scratching sounds and then moving sounds as the mites began to explore the inside of his ear canal. Then, the area occupied by the mites began to itch, followed by noise and pain that intensified.

As the day went on, the itching increased and the sounds in his ear became louder as the mites travelled deeper towards his eardrum. For the next five hours, the mites were very active, but then their activity seemed to level off. At about 11 pm, Lopez went to bed, at which point the mite activity began to increase again. By midnight they were busy biting, scratching and moving about. By 1 am they were making a lot of noise, and around two hours later the itching and scratching was very intense, making sleep almost impossible.

Then, suddenly, the mites seemed to lessen their activities, the noise and itching decreased and a brief sleep became possible. However, it seems that Lopez wasn't the only one sleeping, as the next morning the mite activity began again at 7 am. This pattern of mite activity was repeated the next day and continued. By the third week, the ear was filling up with debris and the hearing in Lopez's left ear had gone. By the fourth week, Lopez estimated that the mite activity had dropped by 75 per cent, and he could feel the mites crawling across his face at night. The mites didn't try to enter his right ear, nor did they bite or cause any itching anywhere else on his body. At the end of one month, he could no longer hear or feel any mite activity and the itching and noises were going. He decided to clean his ear for the first time, and by the sixth week there was no itching and his hearing was normal.

Lopez carried out this experiment twice more on his left ear and, interestingly, he found the last experiment to be less itchy and less painful than the previous ones. By the end of day nine, the mites had stopped biting altogether. He concluded that, perhaps, mammals have an immune response to these ear mites, which is why subsequent infestations are less intense.

In 1994, Lopez was awarded the Ig Nobel Prize in the field of entomology – the Ig Nobel Prizes are a parody of the Nobel Prizes, which are designed to highlight amusing and thought-provoking research. At the ceremony, Lopez recited an original poem about ear mites; he then handed a selection of dead bugs to members of the audience.

After the execution of King Charles I, why did people dab their hankies into his blood?

Charles I (1600–49) was a deeply unpopular king, who engaged in a disastrous power struggle with Parliament, which resulted in the English Civil War. In the First Civil War (1642–5), Charles was defeated; he was then expected to accept Parliament's demands for a constitutional monarchy. Instead, he escaped to the Isle of Wight and attempted to forge an alliance with Scotland. This led to the Second Civil War (1648–9), in which Charles was again defeated. This time, he was captured, tried and found guilty of making war on his own people. He was sentenced to be executed in 1649. Charles was dignified and calm in the face of death, and on the scaffold he said, 'All the world knows I never did begin a war with the two Houses of Parliament … They began these unhappy troubles, not I …'

As the axe came down upon his neck there was a groan from the crowd. The axeman then held Charles's head up to the crowd and blood splattered everywhere. After paying a fee, people hurriedly dipped their handkerchiefs in the king's blood, and they took hairs from his head and beard. They also scraped up bloody earth from beneath the scaffold. People believed that royalty had God-like powers and thought that the king's blood would cure their wounds and illnesses. They wiped their blood-soaked hankies over wounds; some people dabbed it over themselves, each other and their sick children.

After the execution, Charles's head was sewn back on to his body, and he was buried at Windsor Castle. However, in 1813, Royal Surgeon Sir Henry Halford was asked to perform an autopsy on Charles's body. He stole a vertebra from the corpse, which he took home and used as a salt cellar. Apparently, he enjoyed using it to shock his guests at dinner parties. Halford kept the bone for 30 years. However, when Queen Victoria found out, she was not amused, and she ordered that it be returned to Charles's skeleton.

Why did many gladiators commit suicide?

During the heyday of the Roman Empire, the state would often provide lavish entertainment on public holidays. This might consist of theatrical performances and, sometimes, wild animal shows and gladiatorial contests.

Hundreds of thousands of people were sent to their deaths in the arenas of ancient Rome, either through battling other gladiators or being made to fight wild animals. Most gladiators were not willing participants in these contests and were forced to fight, having been drawn from the ranks of slaves, criminals or prisoners of war (although, strangely enough, there were some volunteers). New recruits received harsh training in combat skills, using wooden weapons, in preparation for the contest. Helmets, shields and arm defences were issued to fighters both in training and on the day of the contest.

The vast majority of gladiators were men, but for the novelty factor, occasionally women would be forced to fight. There are even reports of female gladiators fighting with dwarves, which apparently proved very popular. The presence of female gladiators in the arena steadily increased over the years, especially during the reign of Nero, in the first century AD. Eventually the use of female gladiators was outlawed in the early third century BC.

During the build-up to a gladiatorial contest, one bizarre ritual was that on the night before the fight, all the gladiators – who would spend the next day attempting to murder one another – would sit down and eat dinner together. Fans could pay to come and watch these dinners.

On the big day, the gladiator would be expected to fight against wild beasts such as bears and lions or against other unwilling participants. If they were lucky, gladiators could reasonably expect to fight only two or three times before being killed in the arena. Fearful of having an incredibly painful death, many gladiators either tried to escape or commit suicide. To prevent this, the authorities would shackle the gladiators with chains and keep a constant watch over them. Nonetheless, some still managed it.

On one famous occasion, a wealthy politician called Symmachus ordered a number of prisoners to fight in honour of his son. Twenty-nine Germans, who were supposed to fight the next day, decided to strangle one another instead. An even more gross method of suicide was employed by another German, who found a way to kill himself when he was allowed to go to the bathroom. Romans did not use toilet paper, instead, each bathroom would be equipped with a sponge on a stick. The German gladiator, desperate to avoid a terrifying and painful death in the arena, took one of these sponges and forced it down his own throat, suffocating himself.

What is a plate woman?

Some cultures practise a range of extreme and unusual methods to make themselves appear more attractive. Among the Mursi and Surma people of south-west Ethiopia, the adult females are known as 'plate women'. When they are in their early twenties, a small plate, called a labret, is inserted into a slit separating their lower lip and jaw. After some time has passed and the flesh has stretched, the plate is replaced with a larger one. This process is repeated, until the upper lip protrudes as much as 10cm (4in), and the lower lip extends as much as the size of a dinner plate. However, the technique varies from tribe to tribe; some stretch only one lip, some both lips.

Lip plates are worn by women as a form of decoration and as a sign of status. The plates must always be worn in the company of men, but when the women are alone, eating, sleeping or in the company of other women, they are allowed to remove them. When the plate is removed, the women's stretched lips hang down loosely, swaying below their jaw. Ironically, it seems that this bizarre practice started as a way to make the women unattractive to slave traders, in the hope that they would go elsewhere in their search for slave girls, but, eventually, it became regarded as a sign of beauty.

Altering the teeth for aesthetic reasons is another peculiar beauty practice that has been found in cultures around the world. For example, some Australian Aboriginals will chip either one or both of their front incisors, to make them look more attractive. In parts of Africa and Central America, teeth are filed or chipped into points. In Bali, teeth are filed as an important rite of passage for adolescents. Mayans also filed and drilled holes into their teeth so that they could insert jewels.

In parts of Burma, it is seen as very beautiful for women to have unusually long necks. The women of the Padaung tribe are required by local custom to start wearing brass neck-rings at around the age of five. At first, they begin with five brass rings around their necks, but over time this number is steadily increased, and the ladies' necks can reach heights of around 38cm (15in). The neck muscles become so stretched by this practice that it is believed that if an average tribeswoman were to remove the heavy brass rings, her neck would be unable to support her head.

What is urine therapy massage?

One treatment you might not see advertised at your local beauty salon is an Ayurvedic treatment called urine therapy massage. This treatment uses urine, either cold or heated, to massage the body. It is said that 'the best urine to use is the first flow in the morning, about 8 to 10 ounces is most effective'. The urine is then boiled and allowed to cool, before being poured into a bowl and used to perform a body massage. After the massage, the patient is advised not to take a shower or bath for at least two hours.

For centuries people have been availing themselves of urine's supposed curative powers by regularly drinking it, and urine therapy has been regaining popularity in recent years. Also, the fact remains that everybody has drunk their own urine at some point in their life, namely in the mother's womb. As babies urinate, their urine is released into the amniotic sac where it becomes part of the amniotic fluid. Indeed, urine therapy is by no means new. The *Ebers Papyrus* is an Egyptian book on medicine, written in about 1000 BC; it contains 55 recipes for urine therapy. Even the father of medicine, Hippocrates, was an advocate of the practice of uropoty, which means the drinking of urine.

Religious use of urine therapy is well documented in India. The scripts of the ancient Sanskrit text *Damar Tantra*, which date back 5,000 years, advise that drinking urine can rejuvenate the body. Animal urine was also believed to be therapeutic and, in early times, Hindus would accompany their cows to graze in fields and would drink the cow's first urine of the day. Cow's urine was believed, and in fact still is by many Hindus, to have medicinal value.

In which society do the men claim never to fart?

The men of the Chagga tribe in Tanzania undergo a strange initiation ritual. At a given point during puberty the boys of this tribe are taken away to take part in a ceremony in which their anus is said to be blocked with a plug, so that from this point on, those initiated will never need to fart or defecate. Once the ceremony has taken place, the boy in question is required never again to admit to any kind of anal emission, especially in the presence of women, young girls or uncircumcised boys.

On the day of initiation, the boy is taken from his home and is later returned to the tribe, with his bum bleeding. The women are told that his bottom has been sealed, and that from that day forth, the women and children are expected to believe that he will never again fart or do a poo. In actual fact, of course, no operation is ever performed. Instead, all that happens is the boy is forced to sit repeatedly on a bush of thorns, and it's this which causes the bleeding. During the ceremony, the boy is ordered never again to pass wind, or anything else, except in secrecy, where no woman might find out about it. And then, when they eventually reach old age, the men of the Chagga tribe are again taken away, so that the so-called operation can be reversed. After this point, they can once again openly fart and defecate to their heart's content.

In fact, the Chagga's view of masculinity seems to be bizarre in a number of respects. When, for instance, two men of the tribe become blood brothers, they seal the bond by drinking beer that is mixed with saliva and blood.

What is hara-kiri?

From around AD 700 to the 1860s, shoguns (military dictators) ruled Japan, and Japanese warriors called samurai served them. Samurai warriors were expert fighters and carried two swords. Sword makers would test their swords' effectiveness either on corpses or condemned prisoners. They would carry out a series of tests by cutting through body parts, starting with small bones, such as a finger or a toe and then moving on to bigger bones, such as an arm or a thigh bone.

The samurai believed that if you were beaten in battle, the noble thing to do was to commit suicide. They did this by slicing open their abdomen, a gross practice known as hara-kiri or belly cutting. After committing hara-kiri, the warrior would have his head cut off. Individuals also committed hara-kiri if they did something that was shameful, or had dishonoured their family or associates. In fact, the offended people were invited to witness the death.

A Japanese family called the Hojo clan ruled Japan from around 1185 until 1333. In 1333, the city of Kamakura was besieged and captured. When the battle was seen to be lost, the Hojo regents were determined to die like true samurai. In total, 870 samurai and their families committed suicide. One samurai 'cut his body with a long cut from left to right and fell down, pulling out his intestines'. Other samurai cut open their abdomens too, while some are reported to have cut off their own heads.

The samurai showed they were great warriors by collecting the heads of their victims. They chopped off the heads of other samurai warriors, put them into a head bag and got their wife to prepare the trophies for display. This preparation would include applying make-up, dressing the hair and blackening the teeth. Black teeth were considered very fashionable at that time. The samurai would then impress their warrior friends by showing off their head collection. The better the heads looked and the sweeter they smelled, the greater the victory; a perfumed head meant they had killed a top samurai.

In 1213, a battle between samurai warriors resulted in 234 heads being placed along the banks of the Katasegawa River.

What people tickled their throats to induce vomiting?

Roman diners regularly spat and vomited at the table. In fact, Romans were known to tickle their throats with feathers after each meal to induce vomiting, thus allowing them to return to their gluttonous feasting. They even had special bowls in which to spew, although they frequently decided to spit or puke on the floor instead. Slaves had the disgusting job of cleaning up the mess. The puke would have consisted of delicacies such as dormice drizzled with honey, which was a favourite food of the Romans. The philosopher Seneca (3 BC–AD 65) wrote, 'The Romans vomit that they may eat, and eat that they may vomit.' It's amazing anyone had an appetite, you'd think the smell on its own would turn stomachs.

In the Middle Ages, it was considered acceptable to spit during dinner, but only onto the floor. It was also quite proper to belch at the table but not in somebody's face. Picking one's nose was also fine, providing the snot was wiped onto one's clothing or the tablecloth. Guides discussing table manners were written during this period, which observed that spitting was not only a custom, but that people clearly felt the need to spit frequently. However, although spitting was commonplace, an individual was not allowed to spit on or over the table, but he could spit under it. Nor should a person spit into the washbasin when cleaning his mouth or hands, but he could spit beside it. In the 1500s, people who spat on the ground were then expected to tread on it, especially if it contained purulence (ie pus). However, by the late 1600s, it was regarded as indecent to spit in general.

How often did people wash in the 1600s?

From the Middle Ages onwards many people believed bathing was unhealthy and could lead to illness – it was even considered a sin. In the 1600s, people weren't too concerned about personal hygiene. If they bathed at all, the wealthiest people used a wooden or copper tub in front of the fire, in water which would have been heated in the kitchen and then brought upstairs in buckets by the servants.

Soap was very expensive, and so if people did wash, they would only use it on their faces, necks, hands and, occasionally, their feet. Unsurprisingly then, people of the time reeked of BO and had foul-smelling breath. To hide the pungent smell of BO, women carried ornately embroidered bags, tied at the waist, containing aromatic potpourri. In fact, perfume was invented to cover up unpleasant body odours. At this time, cleaning the teeth was done by rubbing them with a piece of cloth and using toothpicks made from wood or ivory to pick out trapped bits of food.

Queen Elizabeth I (1553–1603) was considered something of a neat freak, as she was known to have a bath as often as once a month! However, Elizabethans were fastidious about some things, and many would clean their nails and comb their hair every day.

Legend has it that Queen Isabella of Castile (1451–1504), who was responsible for sponsoring Christopher Columbus's voyage of discovery to the New World, boasted that she bathed only twice in her life – at birth and before her marriage.

Which room contains the most germs – the bathroom or the kitchen?

Dr Charles Gerba, known as Dr Germ by his colleagues, is a microbiologist at the University of Arizona. Dr Germ is renowned as being America's expert on domestic and public hygiene and has appeared on numerous television programmes. He has made quite a name for himself studying public toilets and other places where germs hang out.

Dr Germ carried out a survey and found that, in most homes, the bathroom is actually much cleaner than the kitchen. Surprisingly, the least contaminated place in either room was the toilet seat. Accordingly, Dr Germ concluded that most people would be safer making a sandwich on top of the toilet bowl, rather than in the kitchen. He also quipped, 'That's why your dog likes to drink out of the toilet!'

Moist environments in the kitchen, such as the dishcloth and the kitchen sink drain, were some of the most contaminated with bacteria. However, the worst offender is the kitchen sponge, which can contain up to 50 million bacteria! Faecal bacteria was found in kitchen sponges and dishcloths. Dr Germ found that kitchen sinks are the place where you can find the worst kinds of germs, and thorough wiping of sink and counters with a sponge only serves to spread them all over the kitchen. He also found that 20 per cent of coffee cups contained faecal bacteria, which had almost certainly been transmitted from the sponges that had been used to wash them.

Where else are we likely to encounter germs?

There are an estimated 5,000,000,000,000,000,000,000,000, 000,000,000 bacteria living on Earth – that's five million trillion trillion – and an astonishing number of these live on or around our office desks. According to a study conducted by the famous Dr Germ, the average desk harbours 400 times more bacteria than the average toilet seat.

However, the germiest thing in the workplace is actually the phone. An average phone receiver contains over 25,000 germs per square inch, in comparison to an average toilet seat, which only contains around 49 germs per square inch.

The dedicated microbiologists of the University of Arizona have also tested various public places to determine the most germ-ridden areas. They found that surfaces that were frequently touched were often contaminated with bodily fluids such as blood, spit, mucus and sweat. After you touch these surfaces, your hands then become contaminated by them, so that everything you subsequently touch then becomes contaminated. Then, for most of us, it's only a matter of time before our hands touch a part of our face, and if the nose is touched, it can allow germs to enter the nose and so lead to infection. Research has shown that using soap and water to wash the hands reduces your risk of developing diarrhoea by 45 per cent and decreases your risk of catching other nasty bugs which cause intestinal infections by around 50 per cent.

The most germ-ridden places were found to be play-grounds, nurseries, buses, shopping trolleys, escalator hand-rails and public phones. Perhaps unsurprisingly, Dr Germ is very cautious about which public surfaces he touches. 'Personally,' he recommends, 'I use my knuckle – never my fingertip – to push the elevator button, especially to the ground floor, which is the most contaminated.' Dr Germ also found that women's public toilets contained twice as much poo bacteria as men's, perhaps due to the fact that women are often accompanied by small children and babies who need their nappies changing.

Dr Germ also recommends that when you wash your underwear you make it your last load. He says, 'Basically, if you do undergarments in one load and handkerchiefs in the next, you're blowing your nose in what was in your underwear.' Apparently, freshly washed laundry is heaving with bacteria and a survey showed that half of all homes had faecal material in the washing machines, and as much as 10g (¼oz) of faecal matter was found in underwear. Washing didn't always help get rid of this, either, because most people do a washing machine load along with other clothes, thereby spreading the faecal contamination around.

Dr Germ's study contained a number of other surprising findings. For example, an ATM machine was found to have more germs than a public toilet door handle! One explanation for this may be that hands touching a public toilet's doorknob are more likely to have been washed immediately prior to touching it, compared to those hands which touch an ATM keypad. One study even found faecal matter on the screen of an ATM machine.

The researchers used fluorescent dyes to track the germs that volunteers touched during an average day and to monitor how they spread them throughout their homes. When the household surfaces were exposed to ultraviolet black lights, the result was like the Blackpool Illuminations.

How hygienic are we?

A survey of over 6,000 people was conducted as part of an exhibition entitled Grossology at the Science Museum in London. It revealed that the British have some pretty gross habits. A third of those asked about their personal habits said they picked their nose more than five times a day, and 34 per cent admitted to eating their bogies. There were also regional variations, with the biggest nose pickers being the Northern Irish, 44 per cent of whom admitted to picking their nose more than five times a day. Forty per cent of snot-loving Scots admitted to eating their bogies.

Many men and women admitted to not changing their underwear every day, including 39 per cent of the Northern Irish. Overall, unsurprisingly, women changed their underwear more frequently than men. The men of Kent were particularly shameless, with only 3 per cent of those questioned confessing to a daily change of pants, compared to 78 per cent of Welsh men. Researchers also found that 34 per cent of people had no shame in burping loudly in public and that 29 per cent would fart openly in public. This kind of earthy, primitive charm was particularly pronounced in Essex, where nearly 50 per cent of men had no qualms about farting or belching loudly in public.

However, we Brits are certainly not alone in our mucky habits. In September 2000, the American Society for Microbiology reported the results of a survey that found that of 7,836 people observed using public toilets in five American cities – Chicago, Atlanta, New York, New Orleans and San Francisco – only about two-thirds washed their hands. The glamorous Gothamites of New York were the least likely to wash their hands, with only 49 per cent of them bothering.

What is the worst job in history?

The annals of history are full of disgusting, dangerous and demeaning jobs, but one of the most unpleasant has to have been that of the fuller. In the Middle Ages, this crummy job managed to combine grossness with mind-numbing banality. Fullers worked in the preparation of wool. After the sheep were sheared, a natural grease would remain in the wool. This grease made the cloth both coarse and widely meshed, so the job of the fuller was to get rid of the grease and other unwanted substances from the newly woven woollen cloth. To achieve this, the cloth was soaked in some kind of alkaline solution, and the cheapest alkaline solution available was stale urine, which is full of ammonia.

Of course, urine was always plentiful and bucketloads of it would be obtained from local houses, farms and even public toilets. The next step was the tedious task of stamping on the cloth, while knee-deep in stale urine, for between seven and eight hours to produce a finished piece of thick cloth. However, if insufficient attention had been paid throughout the treatment, it could lead to holes appearing in the fabric. This would ruin the whole cloth, so the fuller would have to be very thorough. The fuller would then rinse the cloth in clean water, take it outside and stretch it out to dry on hooks on a device called a tenterframe. This process of creating tension is the origin of the phrase 'on tenterhooks'.

Another unpleasant profession was that of the tanner, during the Victorian era. A tanner was an extremely skilled craftsman, but the job was very smelly. It was so smelly, in fact, that tanners were required by law to set up their operations on the outskirts of town, due to the noxious stink.

The tanning process would begin after the cow had been slaughtered and skinned. First, the tanner would soften the hide by soaking it in lime and then remove all the rotting meat and fat from it. The fat was useful as it could later be made into soap. The cow's hair would also be removed by being scraped off with a knife. It was important to remove all hairs because after the leather was tanned, the hairs would not come out. Then the leather would be soaked in a gross mixture called bate. It consisted of warmed-up water and faeces, usually dog's shit; this removed the lime and softened the hide. Later, the hide was soaked in tanning fluid for a year, cleaned off, and finally dried out so that leather items could be made from it.

If the tanner's job sounds bad, spare a thought for his suppliers. Tanners needed a constant supply of dog poo, which was provided by somewhat lowlier workers called pure collectors. Their job was at least a simple one – they would roam the streets, looking for dog poo, which they would scoop up, often with their bare hands, and then sell on to people such as tanners.

During the Middle Ages, the job of the squire involved looking after his knight's every need, including caring for the knight's armour and weapons and helping him to train. The squire would also help the knight to dress, but the worst part of the job was undoubtedly cleaning the knight's armour after a heavy day on the battlefield. It took almost an hour to dress a knight in plate armour, which meant there were no quick toilet breaks while fighting. This meant that the knight not only sweated heavily, as tournaments mostly took place during the summer months, but he also urinated and excreted inside the armour.

Therefore, the squire had the unenviable task of cleaning the armour, and to make matters worse, water was in short supply and far too precious to be used for trivial matters like cleaning. Instead, the squire would have to carry out his distasteful chore using an abrasive mixture of sand, vinegar and urine.

From the sixteenth century, it was the trade of the salt-petre man to extract potassium nitrates, also known as saltpetre, from faeces and urine. Saltpetre was in consider-able demand, as it was an important constituent of gun-powder. It was thus vital that the supply of saltpetre be maintained, and so to ensure this, the saltpetre men were given a licence from the king to go into anyone's home and dig wherever they saw fit. This meant they had the right of access to people's houses, barns, stables, outhouses, cellars, latrines, pigpens and manure heaps. They would then dig out the excrement and the sewage-ridden earth of the cess-pit, and cart it away in barrels. How, you may wonder, would they know where to dig? Well, often their sense of smell would suffice, but where there was doubt, the salt-petre men would identify which parts of the soil were rich in saltpetre by tasting it.

Understandably, people weren't keen to have saltpetre men digging up their land, and so to preserve their prop-erty from damage by the ruinous digging, landowners often resorted to bribery. Consequently, it later became an offence to bribe a saltpetre man. And if it wasn't enough that they would make a mess of your property, once the saltpetre men had dug up your earth, they then expected the landowner to supply cheap transport for it. In 1638, saltpetre men even tried to get permission to search for nitrate-rich substances in churches, arguing that, 'women pee in their seats which causes excellent saltpetre'.

What was a dredgerman?

Many of Charles Dickens's (1812–70) works make reference to London's river Thames. In his novel *Our Mutual Friend*, the river plays a central part and serves as a metaphor for the city's filth and corruption – it is covered with slime, which mostly consists of sewage. At the beginning of the novel, two men are found drowned in the Thames by the dredgerman. As disgusting as the river was, and Dickens's account was typically accurate, the Thames provided many poor Londoners with a living. In the late 1800s, the dredgerman's job involved fishing for corpses. In those days, they were kept busy, as the Thames was often littered with corpses. Dredgermen were paid for each corpse they found, but many of them would empty the pockets of the dead before handing the body over to the authorities.

Another similarly unpleasant job of the time was that of the mud lark, although calling it a job may be something of a stretch. Mud larks were scavengers, who spent their time trawling the banks of the Thames, looking for anything of value. In those days, it was common to see old women foraging along the riverbank, carrying a tatty basket or a tin kettle, into which they would put anything of value that they might find. It was not just a job for women either; small children as young as seven years old would also be found searching through the filth. They made a living by paddling and groping for any sort of refuse washed up by the tide on the banks of the river. They poked around in the wet mud for small pieces of coal, chips of wood, bits of old rope, bones or more valuable debris such as copper nails.

In Victorian London, mud larks often had to wade up to their midriffs through excrement and mud while scavenging on the banks of the Thames. They were too poor to buy decent clothing, so they wore filthy rags and no shoes. Consequently, it was common for them to injure themselves or catch infection by standing on nails or glass. But if a mud lark didn't find anything that they could sell before the tide rose, they would most likely go hungry until the tide had next subsided, when they could once again wade through the grimy water.

Are violin strings really made of catgut?

The strings of today's violins are almost always made of synthetic materials, but it is true that, a few centuries ago, they were made from the intestines of animals. However, although this material is known as catgut, it is in fact made from the intestines of sheep, not cats.

Violin-string makers often worked at abbatoirs, so that they could be near to the source of violin strings – the lower intestines of sheep. To produce the strings, the string maker would slice open the sheep's stomach, being careful not to damage the precious intestines, remove the intestine whole and then knead the entire length of the gut to squeeze out any poo that remained stuck inside. The skilled craftsman would then remove all fatty tissues, blood vessels and bile, and clean the intestines thoroughly. Then, the thicker parts of the intestine would be taken away to make sausage skins, while the thinner ends would be soaked in cold water, crushed and then fumigated in a sulphur bath. Finally, the material would be twisted together and dried, resulting in the valuable and melodious violin strings. The whole job required a great level of skill and expertise, but it would also have been rather stinky.

What is phossy jaw?

In Victorian times, many poor girls were forced to work in matchstick factories for 14 hours a day with few breaks, standing the whole time and for very little pay. The girls were even fined for offences as trivial as talking, having dirty feet or dropping matches. These factories were often little more than dingy, dark rooms with working conditions that routinely exposed the girls to a dangerous and unpleasant poison.

In those days, matches were produced simply by dipping small sticks of wood into a toxic substance called white phosphorus. Contact with white phosphorus led to a condition known as phossy jaw, whose nasty symptoms included yellowing of the skin, hair loss, toothache and the jaw swelling up with weeping abscesses. The entire jaw would then begin to rot, and the condition caused the girls to smell terribly. This smell was described as being similar to a cross between stale urine and garlic. The only available treatment was removal of the jawbone, which was an agonising operation that would disfigure the sufferer for life. From 1847 onwards, there was a steady trickle of cases of phossy jaw in London hospitals. In the Bryant and May factory in London alone, there were 51 cases over 20 years. Following an international agreement in 1906, white phosphorus began to be replaced by the relatively safer red phosphorus in the manufacture of matches.

Why did the Wari tribe of the Amazon eat the bodies of their dead relatives?

Throughout history, different cultures have treated human remains in a variety of ways. In our culture, we currently consider it normal and respectful to burn them or freeze them, or even to drain them of blood, pump them full of chemicals, put make-up on them and bury them in the ground. In the past, other societies, such as the ancient Egyptians, felt that bodies should be preserved for eternity through mummification. And, in some primitive societies around the world, from Australia to South America, it was once considered a proper and fitting show of respect to eat the dead.

In the 1960s, a tribe living in the Amazon rainforest practised two subtly distinct types of cannibalism. The Wari tribe would eat their defeated enemies in order to show their anger and contempt for them. On the other hand, when their nearest and dearest died, the Wari believed it was important to demonstrate their love and respect, which they duly expressed by eating them. However, the Wari never ate their own blood relatives. This job was given to their in-laws, and in this society it would have been considered extremely rude not to oblige. The thought of their loved ones being buried and left to rot in the cold, wet ground was not considered dignified. An intact corpse was something painful to view, but if it was eaten, the mourners could deal with their loss more effectively. However, this practice has now ceased.

What caused MPs to flee Parliament in 1858?

In the 1850s, London was a pretty disgusting place. The streets, streams and rivers were choked with sewage, and much of the waste from sinks and toilets ran down old sewers straight into the river Thames. Since most Londoners also got their drinking water from the Thames, it's hardly surprising that many people became sick and even died as a result.

During the long hot summer of 1858, people of central London were plagued by a foul stench. London at this time was nicknamed the Great Stink and its people were called the Great Unwashed. It was vastly overpopulated and the sanitation was poor. The summer was so dry that much of the water in the Thames evaporated, and so the river level became very low. This meant that sewage dumped into the river was not carried out to sea and it became an open sewer. For years, human sewage, slaughterhouse waste, rubbish, dead animals, chemicals from factories and even dead bodies had been dumped into the Thames. Unsurprisingly, the pong became unbearable and the disgusting odour could be smelled from 97 km (60 miles) away.

As the river's fish died out, the riverbanks became covered in a purple-pink mass of squirming, tube worms. Sanitation workers deposited tons of lime into the river to help combat the foul stench and lime-soaked curtains were hung in the windows of Parliament to mask the smell, but eventually the pong got so bad that MPs fled from the Houses of Parliament. Heavy rain finally broke the hot weather, and restored the river to normal levels.

However, the Great Stink prompted Parliament to appoint Joseph Bazalgette (1819–91) to build London's sewer system to take the sewage further downstream away from the city. His system, together with many improvements, is still with us today.

Which famous criminals ate human body parts?

The Butcher of Berlin was the nickname given to Georg Karl Grossmann, who was arrested in 1921, after having killed and chopped up several prostitutes. In particular, he had a preference for plump women. He was caught when neighbours heard him struggling with a woman who was fighting him off. Police burst in and found a woman's murdered body. Grossman gained his nickname because not only did he eat the flesh of his victims, but he also sold a lot of meat on the black market. It is believed that this meat was the flesh of his victims, which he sold in the form of sausages, at a cheap rate – he even had a hot dog stand at a railway station. It's estimated that Grossmann killed around 50 women. At his trial, he showed no remorse and laughed when he was given the death penalty. Later, he hanged himself in jail.

The Russian serial killer Andre Chikatilo, known as the Russian Ripper, didn't sell human flesh as sausage meat, but he did have a penchant for eating genitals. During the 1980s, he consumed the genitals of some 53 young women and children. Being a schoolteacher and Communist Party member, Chikatilo was a respected and trusted member of the local community. This made it easier for him to commit his terrible crimes, as people who knew Chikatilo simply couldn't bring themselves to suspect him of murder. Under normal circumstances he was impotent, but he found that he was sexually aroused by violence and cruelty and could achieve orgasm by stabbing and raping his victims. Chikatilo said it gave him animal satisfaction 'to chew or swallow nipples or testicles'. After he was caught, he confessed and gave a full account of his crimes. In 1994 he was executed, by a single shot fired into the back of his head.

Another very disturbing recent case was that of a German computer technician called Armin Meiwes, who posted an advertisement on an Internet site which read, 'Looking for a well-built 18- to 30-year-old to be slaughtered and then consumed.' Bernd Jurgen Brandes replied to the ad, agreeing to be eaten and so the two men met up on 9 March 2001. On the day, they made a video. One part of this gruesome two-hour video shows Brandes urging Meiwes to slice off his penis, so that the pair can fry and eat it. Meiwes does so, using a knife, and then cooks the penis in garlic. They both shared the penis meal but complained that, after cooking, it was too tough. Brandes joked, 'If I'm still alive in the morning, we can eat my balls for breakfast.'

Hours later, Brandes died of blood loss in Meiwes's bath, having been given large quantities of alcohol, painkillers and sleeping pills, while Meiwes read a *Star Trek* novel. Over the next 10 months, Meiwes ate around 20kg (44lb) of his victim, which he stored in his freezer. Police also found a photograph showing Brandes's amputated foot, which was impaled with a fork, lying on a dinner plate covered with sauce. Meiwes is currently serving a life sentence in a German prison.

How many insect parts do we unintentionally eat?

Realistically, few of the people who read this book will ever deliberately sit down to a meal of fried hairy caterpillars or chocolate-covered cockroaches. However, even if we may not actively choose to eat insects, there seems to be little we can do to avoid them forming some part of our diet, as insect parts will crop up in our food whether we like it or not. In fact, those people who practise insect-eating, or entomophagy to give it its proper name, have pointed out that although only 80 per cent of the world's population eat insects intentionally, 100 per cent of us do eat them in one way or another. According to estimates, the average person consumes around 1kg (2lb 4oz) of insects every year.

Harvard medical entomologist Dr Richard Pollack has eaten numerous bugs, and he states:

> Virtually everything we eat has bugs (entire or parts) within; indeed there are government standards as to the maximum number of bug parts per unit for each type of food. Imagine the phenomenal biomass of insects and mites that get included when cereal crops are harvested and processed.

The US Food and Drug Administration's (FDA) *Food Action Defect Levels* handbook itemises the 'levels of unavoidable defects in foods that present no health hazards for humans'. The following is a list of foods and the amount of insect and rodent parts and other general unpleasantness that are allowed to be contained within them:

- Chocolate may contain up to 60 insect fragments per 100g (3½oz) and an average of less than one rodent hair per 100g (3½oz).

- Macaroni and noodle products are allowed up to 225 insect fragments per 225g (8oz) and no more than 4.5 rodent hairs per 225g (8oz).

- Canned mushrooms should contain no more than 5 maggots of 2mm (1/16in) or longer per 100g (3½oz) of drained mushrooms, and no more than 20 maggots of any size.

- Peanut butter should contain fewer than 30 insect fragments per 100g (3½oz) and an average of less than one rodent hair per 100g (3½oz).

- Canned tomatoes may contain up to 10 fly eggs per 500g (1lb 2oz) and no more than 2 maggots per 500g (1lb 2oz).

- Wheat should average less than 9mg of rodent excreta pellets and/or pellet fragments per 1kg (2lb 4oz).

Why have Indian women been known to throw themselves onto funeral pyres?

The Hindu ritual of sati involves a Hindu wife following her husband to his death by climbing onto his funeral pyre or climbing onto one of her own shortly afterwards, to be burnt to death. Sati originated over 700 years ago and was regarded as a tradition of the noble classes in India. As a widow, a woman loses her property and her social standing, but she does not become a widow until her husband is cremated. Therefore, by performing sati, the woman is said to never lose her status as a married woman, and thus becomes divine.

By the 1800s, more than 500 women a year were immolating themselves, until 1829 when the custom was finally outlawed. However, even since India gained independence in 1947, some 40 cases have been reported, including that of a pretty, well-educated eighteen-year-old girl named Roop Kanwar, in the town of Deorala in 1987. About eight months into their marriage, Roop's husband died of a burst appendix. According to reports, Roop, wearing her wedding sari, climbed onto her husband's pyre, took his head in her hands and urged her brother-in-law to light the fire. He did so without hesitation, and she was engulfed in flames and burnt to death.

However, while thousands of people were present at Roop's sati, there was little agreement about what had happened. Supporters of sati claimed that Roop had calmly seated herself on the pyre and willingly submitted to the flames, without once crying out. Opponents of the practice, on the other hand, said that Roop had tried to escape the flames several times, only to be pushed back by her in-laws. They argued that Roop would have been a financial liability to her husband's family and so was drugged and coerced into submission.

A more recent case of sati occurred in the central state of Madhya Pradesh. In the summer of 2002, a 65-year-old woman named Kuttu Bai was reported to have climbed onto the burning pyre of her dead husband, thereby committing the act of sati. She was watched by a supportive crowd of more than 1,000 people that included her two sons, who made no effort to stop her. Reportedly, the villagers shouted slogans in support of the act. Policeman who attempted to stop the widow's self-immolation were beaten up and prevented from rescuing her.

However, according to reports, Kuttu Bai had not even had a particularly good relationship with her husband, or her eldest son, and there were many who believed she had been forced to her death. Fifteen people, including the woman's two grown-up sons, were arrested over the incident and faced charges of murder and conspiracy. Subsequently, the sons and Kuttu's brothers were found guilty and were sentenced to life imprisonment.

Which well-known drug is made from horse's urine?

Before the introduction of Viagra, Premarin was the most widely prescribed drug in the US. Premarin is a hormone-replacement therapy that contains a combination of oestrogens. When a woman goes through the menopause, her level of oestrogen falls by some 40–60 per cent, which is the cause of many of the problems associated with menopause. Hormone-replacement therapy can help a woman manage the symptoms of menopause, which can include hot flushes, night sweats and vaginal dryness. Premarin comes in a number of different forms, including tablets, patches and vaginal creams. It is also thought to help reduce the risk of osteoporosis and the chances of heart disease in women over 50.

Premarin and other similar products all contain oestrogen derived from pregnant mares' urine, from which the name is also derived – PREgnant MARes' urINe. However, the use of Premarin has recently declined, probably because of widespread public concern about the cruel treatment of the horses from which the drug is obtained. The manufacturers of Premarin keep pregnant mares in stalls and withhold water from them so that their urine becomes more concentrated; this makes the horse oestrogen easier to extract.

What animal mates until he dies from exhaustion?

The male brown antechinus belongs to the same family as the Tasmanian devil. About the size of a mouse, it has short brown hair, a pointed snout and large ears. It is widespread throughout forests in south-eastern Australia, and it feeds on a diet of beetles, spiders and cockroaches. The antechinus is notorious for its short and intense single mating season. At about 11 months old, the males begin a frantic two-week breeding frenzy, in order to father as many offspring as possible. Leading up to the breeding season, males become increasingly aggressive towards one another, as they compete for females. Males and females form pairs, and the male diligently guards her and fights off competitors who want to mate with his partner. Stress hormones in their bodies reach high levels, and this leads to reduced feeding and lowered immune systems, but allows for sustained bonking. In this period, each male will mate for between six and 12 hours at a time.

Unfortunately, after only one mating season, all this furious mating, along with the frequent aggressive clashes with male rivals, result in the animal's demise – he basically shags himself to death.

Has anyone carried out a head transplant?

In the 1950s, Russian surgeon Vladimir Demikhov undertook an innovative experiment to create a two-headed dog. He grafted the head, shoulders and front legs of a puppy onto the neck of an adult dog. Eventually, he created 20 of these hybrids, but most of them died shortly after the surgery because of infection. However, one of the two-headed animals survived for 29 days.

In his book *Experimental Transplantation of Vital Organs*, Demikhov includes photographs of an experiment carried out in 1954: the transplantation of a one-month-old puppy's head and front legs to the neck of an adult dog. The notes imply that the transplanted puppy remained lively and content, but the adult dog would sometimes shake its head and body in attempting to free itself of the unwanted appendage. At one point the adult dog bit the puppy behind the ear, causing the puppy to yelp and shake its head.

Another Demikhov experiment involved attaching a puppy to Pirat, a German Shepherd. This time, the puppy was able to eat and drink on its own, although it didn't actually need to because it received all its nutrients from Pirat. The puppy's foodpipe was not joined onto a stomach; instead it emptied onto the outside of the dog, so when the puppy enthusiastically lapped at a bowl of milk, it dribbled out of the stump of its food pipe and onto Pirat's neck.

Later, Demikhov carried out an experiment that involved cutting dogs into halves. The upper part of one dog would then be attached to the lower part of another and their arteries grafted together. However, cutting through spinal nerves meant that the lower body would be paralysed. Unsurprisingly, these experiments did not win much admiration from the mainstream scientific community.

CHAPTER FIVE

Diseases, cures and tortures

Which king was said to have had a red-hot poker thrust into his anus?

In 1307, Edward II (1284–1327) succeeded his father, Edward I, to become King of England. Despite being homosexual, Edward married Princess Isabella of France; however, this didn't stop him from openly kissing and cuddling his good friend, a flamboyant young knight called Piers Gaveston. Isabella was unhappy with Edward's behaviour, but for many years acted as a loyal and supportive wife and gave birth to four children.

Edward made Piers the Earl of Cornwall and gave him a prominent place in court. This so annoyed the other earls that, in 1312, they seized hold of Gaveston, accused him of treason and cut his head off. Edward was deeply upset about this, but eventually recovered and turned his affections to the Despensers, both the father and the son, who, confusingly, were both called Hugh. It was at this point that Isabella's patience gave way.

She travelled to Paris with her son, the future Edward III, and met an English noble called Roger Mortimer. They became lovers, and together they planned and then successfully carried out an invasion of England. Victory came quickly, as no one was prepared to fight for King Edward and his friends the Despensers, and so within weeks Mortimer and Isabella were in control. They now ruled the kingdom, and Edward was forced to renounce the throne. He was thrown into a dark and damp cell, underneath which the corpses of dead prisoners had been left to rot. He was fed rotten food and given dirty water. Isabella and Mortimer allegedly had the king murdered in 1327, at Berkeley Castle, Gloucester, by having a red-hot poker thrust into his anus. However, Isabella and Mortimer announced that Edward had died from natural causes, and they even attended his burial at St Peter's Abbey in Gloucester.

What was the medicinal use of hangman's rope?

Before the development of modern medicine, many illnesses were treated in ways that we now consider superstitious, wrong-headed or just plain bizarre. For example, in the 1700s, it was believed that the way to cure a headache was to tie a piece of hangman's rope around your skull. Luckily, this was a period in which there were regular public hangings. This meant that there was an abundance of hangman's rope, and so the hangmen were able to make a good second income. The following are a number of other strange remedies from the past:

- Cow dung – was a traditional cure for skin conditions such as ulcers, inflammation, abscesses and boils.

- Urine – the book *Old-Fashioned Remedies* recommends, 'When your feet are sweaty and aching, or if you have got athlete's foot, blisters or bruises, soak your feet in a bowl of hot urine.'

- Frog spit – it was widely believed that a wart could be cured if it was rubbed with frog spit or snails, which should then be impaled on the thorns of bushes. Licking the eyes of a frog was recommended for eye complaints.

- Insects – to help treat a fever it was recommended to eat woodlice that were rolled up into balls, known as pill-bugs. Consuming a spider would also help bring down a fever, as well keeping a spider in bag and hanging it around the neck.

- Mercury – was recommended for syphilis sufferers and was even sometimes injected into the penis. Alternatively, it might be mixed with pig fat, among other substances, and then applied to the genitals. However, this cure would have been fairly disastrous, as mercury is extremely poisonous; it would have caused fever, sores in the mouth and nose, and also made the poor patient's hair and teeth fall out.

Remedies for the plague

There were numerous daft suggestions to help ward off the plague, including the following:

- Catch syphilis.

- Keep dirty goats in your home.

- Fart into a container and release it when the plague is near.

- Smoke tobacco – children as young as three were ordered to smoke, for their own safety.

- Press a dead, dried toad against swollen lymph glands.

Did Little Miss Muffet really eat mashed-up spiders?

Little Miss Muffet sat on a tuffet
Eating her curds and whey,
Along came a spider,
Who sat down beside her
And frightened Miss Muffet away.

The origin of this nursery rhyme is uncertain; however, Little Miss Muffet first appeared in print in Scotland in 1805, although it was probably around for a lot longer. Some historians believe that the nursery rhyme is based on a little girl called Patience, whose father was an eminent English doctor called Thomas Muffet (1553–1604).

Thomas Muffet was passionate about insects, especially spiders, and how they related to medicine. He was a strong believer in the power of spiders to cure nearly any ailment. Most of his remedies consisted of eating spiders, but some were more imaginative. For example, one of Dr Muffet's recommended treatments for cuts or abrasions was to wrap the wound in fresh spider webs, which apparently worked quite well.

He is thought to have instructed his daughter to eat mashed spiders, believing that they would help her recover from colds. In fact, this was a fairly common remedy for colds 200 years ago. And so, Dr Muffet and his daughter Patience may be the origin of the nursery rhyme.

Who did Henry VIII order to be boiled alive?

John Fisher (1459–1535) was the Bishop of Rochester during the reign of Henry VIII. After Fisher allegedly treated his cook poorly, the man, whose name was Richard Roose, decided to take revenge. He did this by putting a special herb, or some believe poison, into the bishop's feast one night. The herb was supposed to give the guests diarrhoea. Unfortunately, Roose seems to have overdone it as 15 guests became ill; two of them suffered such bad diarrhoea that they died. Roose was arrested and found guilty of casting 'a certayne venym or poison into the yeaste or barme wyth whych porrage or gruel was mayde for the famyly of the Byssopp of Rochester and others'. The cook was tried for murder and was sentenced to be hanged until the outraged Henry insisted on a more fitting punishment. He ordered that Roose be boiled alive in his own pot, and for the next five years the punishment for poisoners was to be boiled alive.

Richard Roose was boiled to death in 1532. He was forced into an iron cauldron, and a fire was lit underneath – it took him two hours to die. A historian wrote, 'Because of its novelty, the event attracted a far larger crowd than attended the more commonplace executions of hanging or burning.' Later executions by this method were designed to be more humane – at least they placed the criminal in the cauldron when the water was boiling hot!

However, a few years later Henry VIII ordered the execution of 66-year-old Fisher, for refusing to acknowledge his king as the Head of the Church of England. Fisher had been put on trial and charged with treason, a crime that carried the death penalty. Until his execution he was imprisoned in the tower; and one day his cook decided not to prepare him a meal. When Fisher asked why, the servant replied, 'It was common talk in the city that you should die, and so I thought it needless to prepare anything for you.' Shaking his head, the bishop replied, 'Well, for all that, thou seest me still alive; so whatever news thou shalt hear of me, make ready my dinner, and if thou seest me dead when thou comest, eat it thyself!'

In 1535 Fisher was beheaded, his head was parboiled and stuck on a pole at London Bridge. After a fortnight, it was thrown into the Thames; its place was taken by that of Sir Thomas More.

Which gruesome documentary featured a young woman drilling into her own brain?

Boring a hole into the head, which is also known as trepanning or trepanation, is a practice that was widely used for many centuries as a cure for madness and many other disorders. The ancient Greeks used trepanation as the cure for almost all head injuries. Ancient Egyptians performed trepanning operations to alleviate pressure on the brain that might be caused by conditions such as a stroke. In 1965, after years of experimentation, Dr Bart Hughes bored a hole into his own skull, using an electric drill and a scalpel, having first administered himself with a local anaesthetic using a hypodermic needle. Afterwards, Hughes became a keen advocate of the benefits of his new state of consciousness. People who have been trepanned report an increased ability to concentrate and generally say they feel good for a long while afterwards.

Dr Hughes became a close friend of a young woman called Amanda Feilding, who decided to film her own trepanation in a gruesome documentary called *Heartbeat in the Brain*. In the film, we see her make a cut in her head with a scalpel and then calmly bore through her skull using an electric drill. There is one particularly grisly moment when blood spurts out of Amanda's head and she turns smiling towards the camera. Amanda, who twice ran unsuccessfully as a UK parliamentary candidate, wanted the public to receive free trepanation on the National Health Service.

What was found in Genghis Khan's hand when he was born?

Genghis Khan (c.1162–1227) was a fearsome Mongolian warrior, and his Mongol army killed hundreds of thousands of people across Asia and Europe as he conquered more land than anyone else in history. Genghis was born with a big clot of blood in his right hand, which the Mongols believed to be a sign that he would be a powerful warrior.

Genghis Khan died in his sixties in 1227. As legend has it, his remains and treasures were taken 322km (200 miles) by his most loyal troops, who killed every living thing in their path, to prevent anyone from ever discovering the grave site. Horses trampled over his grave to shield it further from discovery, and the party responsible for his burial were also killed. Seven hundred years later, the exact location and contents of his tomb are still unknown.

After Genghis Khan's secret burial, his sons and grand-sons continued to expand the Mongol Empire. One of Genghis's sons, Toluy, was a cruel and sadistic madman, just like his father. After massacring many people in a city, he was told that some people had escaped death by hiding among the bodies and pretending to be dead. Determined that this mistake should not be repeated, on his next massacre he ordered all the corpses' heads to be cut off and arranged in pyramids – one for men, one for women and one for children. Other Mongol warlords thought this was a good idea and so began a tradition of warriors building large towers of severed heads.

A study published in 2003 estimates that 8 per cent of men across a large portion of Asia are descended from Genghis Khan. This astonishing revelation is based on DNA testing.

Who was Typhoid Mary?

Worldwide, up to 17 million people suffer with typhoid fever annually, with an estimated 600,000 deaths. Typhoid fever is an infection caused by the bacteria, *Salmonella typhi*. It is a form of food poisoning that, these days, is usually caused by shellfish grown in water contaminated with sewage, or by eating food that has been contaminated by the hands of another sufferer. Typhoid victims suffer symptoms including fever, severe headache, nausea, diarrhoea and abdominal pain, and the disease can be fatal. Fortunately, anyone travelling to a country where typhoid fever is a problem can get vaccinated.

The first identified typhoid carrier in the US was an Irish immigrant called Mary Mallon (1870–1938). She is believed to have been responsible for hundreds of people contracting typhoid and was consequently dubbed 'Typhoid Mary'. She was born in Ireland and emigrated from there to the US when she was 14 years old. By 1906, Mary had worked as a cook for many wealthy families in New York. In 1906, she was working for the Warren family. A month later, half the members of the household began to fall ill, including Mrs Warren, two of her daughters and three of the servants. Mary did not become ill and left the house just three weeks after the typhoid outbreak.

A man called George Soper, a sanitary engineer, was hired to find the cause of the outbreak. After a thorough investigation he came to the conclusion that it was Mary who was responsible. He confronted Mary, who angrily denied ever having typhoid fever. Fortunately, her employment agency gave him a list of some of Mary's previous employers. He subsequently discovered that seven of the eight families for whom she'd worked during the previous ten years had suffered an outbreak of typhoid while Mary worked as their cook. Finally, in 1907, the police forcibly took Mary to a hospital, where she was found to be a carrier of typhoid. She was detained for three years, but was released in 1910 after promising she would not work as a cook, or with food in general. However, after a while Mary disappeared, and in a hospital in New York there was an outbreak of 25 cases of typhoid fever. Three months prior to the outbreak, a new cook called Mrs Brown had been taken on – this, of course, turned out to be Mary Mallon. She again disappeared, but was later caught and detained in a hospital until her death in 1938. Throughout her life, Mary continued to deny vehemently that she had ever carried or transmitted typhoid, despite all the medical evidence to the contrary.

Why did Aztec priests rip out the still-beating hearts of their victims?

The Aztecs of Mexico, whose empire flourished from 1427 to 1521, are infamous for their human sacrifices. They were a warlike people, and their armies set out to invade and take over all neighbouring areas. When they did so, they would take back thousands of captives to their capital city, Tenochtitlan. They were imprisoned in wooden cages and well fed, until their time came to be killed as a human sacrifice.

The Aztecs were a polytheistic people, which means that they worshipped many gods, rather than just one. They believed that these gods provided them respectively with rain, sunshine and everything else they needed to live; in return they offered human sacrifices. In fact, they thought that the gods would be angry and might destroy the world if they didn't offer sacrifices. Around 20,000 people a year were believed to be sacrificed by the Aztec priests. However, in 1487, an unprecedented 80,400 captives were sacrificed during the emperor Ahuitzotl's reconsecration of the Great Pyramid of Tenochtitlan.

The Aztec priests painted their bodies black in order to symbolise religion and war. Their hair was matted with blood from human sacrifices and they filed their teeth to sharp points. They would also wrap themselves in cloaks made from the skins of their previous victims.

Most prisoners were sacrificed by having their hearts cut out with a sharp knife, while other captives had their heads chopped off. However, there were also much slower and nastier ways of being killed, which included being thrown into a lake and left to drown, or being skinned alive. If you happened to be unhealthy, scarred, diseased, fat or ugly, you might consider yourself lucky, as the Aztecs would not choose you for sacrifice. Instead, you would have been forced to work as a slave.

On the big day, the prisoners would be given a herbal potion, to make them feel drowsy. Soon afterwards, they were walked up the steps of the temple at the centre of Tenochtitlan, where the victim would be laid onto a stone slab. The prisoner's abdomen would be sliced open with a knife made of flint, and then the priest would tear out the still-beating heart from the victim's chest, before offering it up to the gods. Next, they would cut off the head, which would be displayed in a skull rack, along with hundreds of others. The prisoner's blood was poured down the temple steps, and the limbs were given to the lucky warrior who had captured the human sacrifice. Naturally, he would make a delicious meal out of the remains; in particular, the hands and thighs were regarded as delicacies.

Between 1519 and 1521, Tenochtitlan was invaded by groups of Spanish soldiers, who used guns, horses and vicious dogs to fight the Aztecs. However, their most effective weapon turned out to be a tiny germ. One of the soldiers was carrying a highly infectious viral disease called smallpox, and in the course of the invasion, he inadvertently managed to spread the deadly smallpox germs to the Aztec people. Having never been exposed to smallpox before, they had no immunity and thousands of Aztecs died as a result. In fact, it's believed to have killed approximately half the Aztec population in less than six months. In 1521, the Spaniards looted Tenochtitlan of its innumerable treasures and its buildings and temples were burnt or pulled down. A new capital, Mexico City, was built on its site.

Which infection causes bleeding from the eyes?

One of the most frightening viruses to come out of the African continent is the Ebola virus. This disease is poorly understood, and the causes of an outbreak are unknown.

However, bats have been implicated, as it seems possible that they may be able to carry the disease, without displaying any symptoms. Outbreaks of Ebola first occurred in the Sudan and the Democratic Republic of Congo (then Zaire) in 1976, and since then more than 1,200 people infected by the virus have died from it.

The Ebola virus causes a number of horrible symptoms including high fever, headache, severe pain, red eyes, vomiting and diarrhoea. As the disease progresses, it can cause bleeding from every opening in the body. This is because the virus causes the blood vessels to break down, allowing blood to seep out into the body. Blood will then flow freely from the nose, eyes, ears, gums, vagina and rectum. Victims die of organ failure or excessive blood loss, and most of those infected die within two weeks.

Ebola is a highly contagious disease that is generally transmitted via person-to-person contact through infected body fluid or through using contaminated needles, but in certain stages it can be transmitted by as little as a handshake. Close contact with the corpses of victims can also spread the virus if they are handled without the wearing of suitable protective clothing. Fortunately, Ebola seems unlikely to develop into a pandemic, because it kills its victims faster than it can spread, and so it burns itself out before travelling too far.

Why might the mention of a goat's tongue have struck fear into the hearts of medieval prisoners?

In the Middle Ages, there were a range of clever and inventive torture methods, designed to punish or force a confession out of you. In a punishment known as the goat's tongue, or tickling torture, the victim's feet would be placed into wooden stocks and covered with salt. Goats love salt, and they will happily continue to lick feet which are covered in it for hours. Although the sensation starts out as initially being little more than a tickle, pain soon follows, as the goat's rough tongue causes the soles of the feet to blister and become sore. By the time the goat's tongue reaches bone, a confession is usually forthcoming. Vlad the Impaler (1431–76) of Transylvania enjoyed using this torture on Turkish prisoners. Salt water would be continually dripped onto their feet from above, and enthusiastic goats would be released.

Another unpleasant torture technique of the Middle Ages was the rack. This nifty device was used to extract confessions, and it was introduced to the Tower of London in about 1420 by the Duke of Exeter. The torture rack consisted of a strong wooden frame fitted with a large roller at each end. The prisoner would be laid on the frame, with ropes attached from the rollers to his ankles and wrists. If the prisoner did not confess to his crime, the rollers would be turned and the body slowly stretched, pulling the limbs in opposite directions, until the joints of the limbs would eventually become dislocated, resulting in excruciating pain. The Spanish Inquisition was also fond of this method.

Guy Fawkes (1570–1606) was put on the rack in 1605 and was tortured for ten days at the Tower of London, until he confessed the names of the other members of the Gunpowder Plot. He was so severely injured that he had to be carried to the scaffold for his execution.

During the reign of Elizabeth I, many Catholic priests were executed as traitors. English Jesuit Edmund Campion (1540–81) was jailed for heresy, after refusing to recant his Catholicism. He was tortured but, even when iron spikes were driven under his finger and toenails, he refused to recant. He was later placed on the rack which caused extreme agony, but he still refused to recant. It is said that when he came off the rack, he was 10cm (4in) taller than before. Campion was given a final chance to renounce his Catholic faith in exchange for his freedom, but his loyalty to the Pope proved too strong. In 1581, he was executed as a traitor, being hanged, drawn and quartered at Tyburn, London.

Thumbscrews were handy, pocket-sized contraptions that were highly effective at inflicting excruciating pain. The victim's fingers were placed inside the instrument and slowly crushed, as the torturer turned the handle on top. Some cunning thumbscrews even had little studs inserted inside them to increase the suffering of the victim. An over-enthusiastic torturer would sometimes crush the finger to a pulpy mess! In Scotland, thumbscrews were known by the rather cute name of 'thumbkins' and were used until the end of the seventeenth century.

The same instrument was also used to crush victims' toes, and even bigger variants were used to crush victims' feet, knees and elbows. Another devious device was the head crusher which, as you might imagine, was designed for applying pressure to the head.

What does it mean to be hanged, drawn and quartered?

From the thirteenth century until the 1800s, the penalty ordained in England for high treason was the extremely gruesome method of being hanged, drawn and quartered. The traitor would be dragged to the scaffold on a wooden frame (called a hurdle) by a horse – this is one possible interpretation of the word 'drawn'. Then he was hanged by the neck until near to death. Next, he was taken down from the gallows, cut open, disembowelled (his internal organs removed) and his genitals were cut off. This all occurred while he was still alive. He would watch as his body parts were tossed into a fire and burnt. The body would then be cut into four parts, that is to say, quartered, before finally being beheaded. Typically, the various parts would then be put onto spikes and displayed publicly.

In 1757, Robert Francois Damiens, a former soldier in the French army, was executed for the attempted assassination of Louis XV. The execution was public, with a large crowd attending the particularly gruesome scene. Prior to the execution, Damiens was kept strapped to an iron bed to prevent him from committing suicide, although he did manage to bite off his tongue, in the hope that he might bleed to death. To stop him doing this again, the guards pulled out his teeth. Then, Damiens was tied to a scaffold and burnt with red-hot pincers on his chest, arms, thighs and calves. As he was being burnt, Damiens 'gave a very loud and continuing cry, which was heard at a great distance from the place of execution'. The hand in which he had held the knife, with which he had attempted to kill the king, was then burnt off, using sulphur and burning oil. Next, molten wax, lead and boiling oil were poured into his wounds. Ropes were then tied to his arms and legs and attached to horses, which were made to run in opposite directions, so that his limbs would rip off. Unfortunately, his joints wouldn't tear, so the executioner had to cut through them with a knife. Damiens was seen to look at his severed limbs, before dying. As soon as he appeared to be dead, his remains were thrown onto a fire.

Damiens's friend, the infamous lover Casanova, who witnessed the execution, wrote in his memoirs, 'I was several times obliged to turn away my face and to stop my ears as I heard his piercing shrieks, half his body having been torn from him.'

Another brutal and common method of punishment was known as the wheel. The wheel always killed its victim, but it did so very slowly and painfully. One variation of this method involved tying a victim to a large wooden wheel, like a cartwheel, so the limbs were hanging over its sides. The executioner would then use a metal bar or pole to break the limbs, until they became so pulverised that they would fit nicely around the outside of the wheel. This allowed the executioner to roll the criminal easily around town. Sometimes, through the openings between the spokes, the torturer would break each bone separately, finally killing the prisoner by hitting him across the chest. However, occasionally the executioner would break the man's ribs, and the wheel would then be mounted on a tall pole, so that birds could feed from the still-living prisoner. He would remain there until his death.

The English were particularly fond of another brutal punishment, the pleasant-sounding *peine forte et dure*, or 'pressing to death'. English Common Law stated that a prisoner had to plead either guilty or not guilty, and until a prisoner gave a plea a trial couldn't be held, so it was common for those arrested to be pressed to plea. It meant literally pressing the accused's body with heavy weights until he gave a plea. If he refused to plead, the prisoner was laid on the ground, naked, and his arms and legs were drawn with cords fastened to several parts of the room. Then, increasingly heavy weights, of iron, stone or lead would be piled on his chest.

One reason prisoners were reluctant to plead was that if they admitted guilt, they would be hanged, which in those days was a lingering and painful death – although pressing wasn't much better. More importantly, as a convicted criminal, all their possessions would be taken away, whereas if they said nothing, even though they would be pressed to death, they would die without being convicted, thereby saving their families from a life of poverty.

In the late 1600s in the American colonies, an 80-year-old farmer called Giles Corey was accused of witchcraft during the Salem witch trials. He refused to plead and so chose to be pressed to death, as he wanted to ensure his wealth was passed on to his family. Now and then the torture was halted to give Corey the chance to plead, but all he said was, 'More weight!' He was tortured for two days, before finally suffocating to death.

Why was Mary Tudor nicknamed Bloody Mary?

When Mary Tudor (1516–58) became queen in 1553 she was determined to return England to Catholicism. In 1554, Protestants were horrified when she married her cousin, the Catholic King Philip II of Spain, and ordered hundreds of Protestants either to convert to Catholicism, or be burnt to death. She ordered 288 Protestants to be burnt at the stake, earning her the nickname Bloody Mary. She believed that fire burnt away all evil, allowing the purified souls to go straight to heaven. To make death quicker, and a little kinder, the executioners would sometimes strap gunpowder to the victim's body.

When Mary came to the throne, two Protestant bishops called Hugh Latimer and Nicholas Ridley were arrested and tried for heresy. At the trial, the accuser pointed at Latimer and Ridley and demanded, 'Swear allegiance to the pope, confess your heresies, and you will live.' Both men refused and in 1555 they were burnt together in the centre of Oxford, in front of a large crowd. The following famous excerpt from John Foxe's *Book of Martyrs* (1583) describes how they were burnt:

> So they came to the stake. Dr Ridley, entering the place first, looked towards the Heaven. Then, seeing Mr Latimer, with a cheerful look, he ran and embraced him saying, 'Be of good heart, brother, for God will either ease the fury of the flame, or else strengthen us to endure it.' Dr Ridley's brother brought him a bag of gunpowder and tied it about

his neck. Then they brought a lighted faggot and laid it at Dr Ridley's feet. Mr Latimer said, 'Be of good comfort, Dr Ridley, we shall this day light such a candle, by God's grace, in England, as I trust never shall be put out.' He then cried out, 'Father of Heaven, receive my soul.'

Other unfortunate victims included Lady Jane Grey (1537–54) and her husband, Guildford Dudley, who were tried for high treason in 1553. Lady Jane had to watch her husband's execution. He was crying as his head was chopped off, and Lady Jane's execution followed shortly after. She was buried underneath the floor in the Tower of London, and her ghost is said to walk the Tower to this day. According to the legend, her ghost appears every year on the anniversary of her execution, as a white shimmering figure that floats, strolls or glides around the Tower, and then slowly withers away.

Which sultan hacked off the heads of men with fat necks?

In 1623, when he was only five, Murad IV (1612–40), also known as Murad the Cruel, became ruler of the Ottoman Empire, an enormous area which stretched from Jerusalem to Constantinople. During his younger years, his dominating mother, Sultana Kosem, effectively ruled through him.

When he grew older, Murad was mean and sadistic. He would sometimes walk through streets accompanied by an executioner, and if he didn't like the look of a person, or if they acted in what he considered to be a strange way, he would have them executed – at one point anyone considered to have a fat neck was killed on the spot. Another time, while out hunting, he came across some women happily singing while having a picnic. The noise displeased him and so he ordered them to be drowned. He also enjoyed shooting servants and members of his harem.

Murad hated smoking, and believed it made people infertile; in fact, he was so opposed to it that he issued a law stating that anyone found smoking would be killed, either by beheading or being hanged, drawn and quartered. Astonishingly, thousands continued to smoke and many met a grisly demise. Murad's cruel example was followed in Persia, where merchants caught selling tobacco were executed by having molten lead poured down their throats.

In 1640, at the age of 28, he died of cirrhosis of the liver, a result of drinking too much alcohol. Ironically, during his time in power, he had also banned alcohol as well as tobacco. On his deathbed he commanded that his brother Ibrahim should be executed and wanted his head cut off and brought to him as proof of his death. However, before this could be done Murad died and Ibrahim became the new sultan. Unfortunately he was just as mad as his brother Murad.

How long does a head remain conscious after being guillotined?

The guillotine is named after a French physician, Joseph-Ignace Guillotin (1738–1814), who, ironically, didn't agree with the death penalty. In 1789 he suggested using this machine to execute criminals, as it was a less painful method of execution than other methods being used, such as hanging. He was horrified that his name was given to it, and when he died in 1814, after the government refused to change the name of the device, his children changed their name so as not to be connected with it.

In France, during the time the guillotine was used, doctors carried out studies to find out if a person's head could remain alive after being decapitated. To research this, the doctors would ask those about to be executed if they would try to keep blinking their eyes after their head had been chopped off. According to reports, some of the heads continued to blink for up to 30 seconds after being cut off, although it is unclear whether or not this was due to the person blinking on purpose, or simply an involuntary reaction.

In late 1905, a French physician called Beaurieux carried out some experiments on the head of a prisoner called Languille, immediately after his head was chopped off. He described his experiments, 'Here then is what I was able to note immediately after the decapitation: the eyelids and lips of the guillotined man worked in irregularly rhythmic contractions for about five or six seconds.' He went on:

I called in a strong, sharp voice, 'Languille!' I then saw the eyelids slowly lift up ... Next Languille's eyes very definitely fixed themselves on mine and the pupils focused themselves ... I was dealing with undeniably living eyes which were looking at me. After several seconds, the eyelids closed again ... It was at that point that I called out again, and, once more, without any spasm, slowly, the eyelids lifted and undeniably living eyes fixed themselves on mine with perhaps even more penetration than the first time ... I attempted a third call; there was no further movement – and the eyes took on the glazed look which they have in the dead ...

The guillotine was last used in France to execute a Tunisian immigrant for the rape and murder of a young girl, in 1977. It was banned in 1981, together with capital punishment, by President François Mitterrand.

What is the worst sound in the world?

It's official, the most unpleasant sound in the world is that of a person vomiting. A survey was carried out to identify the world's worst sound, and, perhaps unsurprisingly, vomiting was voted as the sound that made most people want to cover their ears. The sound was recreated by an actor using a diluted bucket of baked beans, to mimic the sound of vomit cascading into a toilet.

The study, set up by Trevor Cox, a professor of acoustic

engineering at Salford University, asked for people's opinions on 34 sounds. These were hosted on a website, in the hope of learning what makes certain noises so universally disgusting. The survey attracted over 1.1 million votes from around the world. People listened to sounds such as a dentist's drill, fingernails scraping down a blackboard and aircraft flying past, before rating them in order of offensiveness. Microphone feedback was judged to be the second most unpleasant sound, while joint third were the sounds of babies crying and the scrapes and squeaks of a train on a track. Surprisingly, the sound of snoring was deemed only the twenty-sixth most objectionable.

What is gas gangrene?

One infection that you definitely do not want to suffer from is gas gangrene, which is an even more severe form of gangrene. Although rare, it carries a high risk of death, and is extremely painful. It typically results from deep wounds becoming infected, usually through injury or surgery. After an injury to the body, there may be a poor supply of blood to the tissues, and as blood carries oxygen, this lack of oxygen can cause the flesh to die.

Gas gangrene occurs as a result of infection by clostridium bacteria. Under low oxygen conditions, these bacteria produce toxins that cause tissue death and other associated symptoms. After an injury, clostridium spores can find their way into the deep wound, germinate and grow in the dead tissue, causing symptoms such as swelling and severe pain in the affected area. One very unpleasant symptom is that the bacteria produce gases under the skin. This can cause a crackling sensation when the skin is touched, known as crepitation, which is due to the movement of these gas bubbles.

The skin over the wound may rupture to reveal necrotic (dead tissue) muscle, which will have turned black; it will emit a foul-smelling, watery or frothy discharge. If sufferers of gas gangrene are treated quickly, 80 per cent of patients will survive. However, if it affects areas such as the abdominal wall or the bowel, the prognosis is poor. The most common treatment involves surgically cutting out the affected area, or, in many cases, amputation of the limb.

Is it possible to catch gonorrhoea from an inflatable doll?

Gonorrhoea is a sexually transmitted disease caused by a bacterium, Neisseria gonorrhoea, which can grow and multiply easily in the warm, moist areas of a person's sexual organs. This bacterium can also grow in the mouth, throat, eyes or anus. Symptoms of gonorrhoea in men include a burning sensation when urinating and a white, yellow or green discharge from the penis. Sometimes men with gonorrhoea also get painful or swollen testicles.

In 1993, the following story was published in a medical journal called *Genitourinary Medicine*. A Norwegian physician, Harold Moi, took a job working for a venereal diseases clinic in Nuuk, Greenland. One of his patients was the captain of a trawler, who arrived at the clinic with symptoms similar to those of gonorrhoea. A blood test confirmed that he was indeed suffering with gonorrhoea; however, the origins of the disease were something of a mystery. The skipper had been at sea for three months, and the symptoms had appeared towards the end of his voyage. As gonorrhoea takes no more than 30 days to appear, it was evident that the man must have caught the disease while at sea. However, the boat's crew were all male, and the skipper insisted that he had never had a homosexual experience, so how could he have contracted it? The mystery was resolved when the captain confessed that one night, he had gone to a crewman's cabin and borrowed the man's inflatable doll, without asking his permission. A few days later, he had noticed the first symptoms of the disease.

It seems that the owner of the doll had used it shortly before the skipper, and he was also found to have gonorrhoea; indeed, he had it much worse than the skipper. It seems that he had caught the disease from a girl he'd slept with before going to sea and then inadvertently passed it on to his captain, via the inflatable doll.

Who drinks fresh cow's blood?

Like farmers the world over, the Masai people of northern Tanzania keep cattle for their milk, meat, hides and to help with the work of the farm. However, the Masai also have another, more unusual, use for their cattle. To give them strength, they also drink the cow's blood. However, to do this, they don't need to slaughter the cow. Rather, they simply drain the blood by cutting one of the cow's veins, and allowing the blood to pump out into a cup, resulting in a fresh supply of warm blood. Sometimes, the Masai drink the blood as it comes; at other times, they mix it with sugar or simply let it clot, and then divide it into portions. They also give a mixture of cow's milk and blood to the sick to help them recuperate, and to new mothers, so that they might regain their strength after giving birth. Apparently, the cows are usually fairly untroubled by being tapped in this way and are unharmed by the process. A similar practice was carried out by the Mongol warriors of Genghis Khan, who sometimes drank the blood of horses while engaged in battle.

If the idea of eating clotted blood strikes you as bizarre, you might consider the traditional English dish of black pudding, which is a staple ingredient of a cooked breakfast in many parts of the country. Black pudding, as made in the UK, is a blend of onions, pork fat, oatmeal, flavourings and clotted blood, usually pigs' blood.

CHAPTER SIX

The Final Chapter

Who gives massages to dead people?

What could be nicer than a long, soothing massage? Massages help to aid relaxation, and tease out our bodily aches and pains. However, massages are not restricted to the living. Dead people also receive massages but for somewhat different reasons. Massage of the dead serves part of the modern embalming process. Embalming has been carried out for a wide range of reasons down the ages, but these days it is mainly designed to preserve the body so that it can be viewed at a funeral ceremony.

The ancient Egyptians were so skilled at embalming bodies that thousands of them have been found intact over the last millennium. They believed that a person's spirit would return to the body after death, which meant the body must be kept in good condition and not be allowed to deteriorate. The ancient Egyptians used spices, herbs and salt to preserve dead bodies. First, they would remove the body's internal organs through the anus and then scoop the brain out through the nostrils, using a metal hook. Although methods varied, many Egyptian embalmers would then use linen strips soaked with resin to pack into the empty skull. The organs would be cleaned and then mixed with spices, herbs and resins, before being put back into the body or placed in jars. The inside of the body was washed with spiced wine and then allowed to dry out by being immersed in salt. After a few months, the body would be cleansed, stuffed and anointed with oils and resins in order to deter insects. Finally, the incisions were closed up and the body was bandaged; the bandages were held together with gum or glue, resulting in a beautifully preserved mummy.

In modern times, the embalming process is generally referred to as cosmetic embalming; its main purpose is to improve the appearance of the body and prevent deterioration leading up to the funeral. Modern embalming fluid consists of a solution of formaldehyde, often containing pink dye. This solution is injected into the blood vessels, usually via the carotid artery, which is found in the neck. First, the embalmer will insert a tube into a vein, so that blood can be drained from the body. Then, the embalmer massages the body's limbs and hands, to help the blood flow out, clear any blood clots and encourage the flow of embalming fluid as it moves through the body.

The pink dye added to the embalming fluid helps to add colour to the skin – it gives it a more healthy, lifelike appearance. The fluid also helps to plump out the deceased's features, so that they look less tired and drawn. The embalmer will also arrange the dead person's hair and use make-up to make them look their best for when they receive visitors. Massage cream may also be applied to the face and hands to prevent dehydration, and also to aid the massage of the tissues during the embalming process.

What happens to the body after death?

If a corpse is exposed to the elements in hot conditions, it can become a skeleton in around a month. By contrast, if it is buried 1.8m (6ft) underground, even without a coffin, it can take more than ten years. Of course, if dead bodies are not embalmed they quickly begin to putrefy.

Upon death, the muscles relax and blood pools in body parts closest to the ground, giving the underside skin a darkened appearance. The top of the body will become a greyish-white colour. Within minutes, flies, which can smell the corpse's odour from at least a mile away, will arrive on the body. They lay thousands of eggs which soon develop into maggots. The maggots will feed enthusiastically on the corpse's organs and tissues – they can reach adulthood in three weeks. Insects and larvae that feed on and inhabit a corpse are useful to murder investigators as they can help them to determine the date of a person's death.

Stiffening of the corpse occurs within six hours of death, in a process known as rigor mortis, but, after a day, the body slowly relaxes again. From 48 hours after death, bacteria living in the body, especially the colon, begin to effect the decomposition of the body. Beginning on the lower abdomen, the skin becomes a greenish colour; this spreads to the rest of the body, which, by now, will be producing a horrific stench. Gas produced by the bacteria causes the body to bloat, and it turns the skin from green to purple and then to black. The build-up of gas forces the intestines to be pushed out of the body, through the vagina or rectum. This gas also produces a foul stench, as it forces copious amounts of putrid bloodstained fluid to come out of the mouth, nose and other bodily orifices. This is why coffins are made with lids that can burp so that the gas can escape.

Within a week, the skin may develop putrid blisters that burst. Soon, large patches of skin are shed, in a process which is known as skinslip – the skin of the hand can slough off like a glove. Some of the organs such as the eyeballs and brain liquefy. After a few weeks, teeth, nails and hair loosen and may fall off, and much of the body turns into a semi-liquid state. Later, the abdomen and chest areas burst open and the body dissolves.

Historically, many cultures have been petrified of the dead returning to haunt them, and these fears have formed the basis of many of today's burial rituals. The Saxons used to cut off the feet of their dead, to prevent them from walking around at night. In northern Europe, people went to extreme lengths to make sure the dead remained dead. Chopping off the head and feet of the corpse and tying its hands together were commonplace. They took no chances on the risk of being haunted and digging a 1.8m (6ft) deep hole would help to ensure this. Lids of coffins were nailed on tightly, not to prevent the corpse from falling out but to keep it from jumping out at the mourners. After the coffin was lowered into the grave, a large rock was placed on top, followed by dirt and then another big slab of stone was dragged on top to ensure that the dead body could not escape. This second slab of rock eventually evolved into the tombstone.

In Britain, the custom of wearing black and a veil over the head wasn't originally intended as a sign of respect for the dead. Rather it was meant to help hide the identities of mourners from any bad spirits hanging around in the graveyard, which might otherwise cause them harm.

Why did undertakers prick holes into corpses?

After a person dies, the bacteria which are already present in the body begin to increase dramatically in numbers as the immune system can no longer keep them in check. As these bacteria munch away at the corpse, they produce a huge build-up of gas inside the body which causes it to change shape in extraordinary ways: the eyes and tongue protrude, the abdomen will distend, the lips swell and the breasts and genitals balloon in size.

However, this build-up of gases is not just unsightly, it can also be dangerous. If the body was to burst and discharge its gases, the noxious fumes would cause people to vomit or even faint. Consequently, undertakers and gravediggers developed various techniques to deal with these risks. Gravediggers, when they opened a coffin, would immediately flee to a safe distance and stay there until the corpse gas had been sufficiently dispersed. Another custom was to burn paper or straw in graves, while some men believed a mouthful of garlic would protect them from the putrefaction of the corpses. Cases have even occurred of gravediggers being suffocated while thrusting a pickaxe into an abdomen distended with gas.

During the 1800s, coffins used to be tapped to allow the escape of gas. This tapping process involved boring a hole into the coffin that permitted the gas to pass through it. The gas would then be ignited, producing a flame that lasted from around ten minutes to half an hour. On occasions, the build-up of corpse gas could be so intense that it caused the coffins to bulge or even explode.

Another method of releasing gas from bloated corpses involved undertakers pricking tiny holes in the body and then holding a candle to the openings. Long blue flames would appear that were fuelled by the gases escaping from the corpse. These flames would continue to burn until all the gas was gone.

What was a waiting mortuary?

During the seventeenth and eighteenth centuries, the rudimentary nature of medicine meant that there was a risk that people who were comatose or otherwise incapacitated being misdiagnosed as dead. Consequently, many people in Europe and the US were terrified of being buried prematurely. This led to a plethora of pamphlets and books on the phenomena of apparent death and premature burial.

A German physician called Christoph Wilhelm Hufeland also took a great interest in premature burial, and he believed that putrefaction was the only certain sign of death. He also thought that when a person died they first entered into a state of deep unconsciousness, or death trance, which was indistinguishable from real death and could last for a long while. However, Hufeland argued, the death trance was not always fatal. A person could sometimes awaken from this state, which meant that there was a risk that they might be buried alive.

To solve this problem, in 1791, Hufeland built a waiting mortuary in Weimar in Germany; this consisted of a corpse chamber, with eight beds for the deceased. A fire was kept alight continually and steam from boiling water was fed through underground pipes to the corpse chamber; this was designed to help ensure that any bodies which actually were dead would rot quickly, and thus demonstrate the fact of their death. To help disguise the smell of rotting flesh, bouquets of flowers were placed around the beds to perfume the air.

Additionally, there was an attendant employed to look out for signs of life, in case any of the bodies turned out to have merely been in a death trance. Another gruesome and smelly job of the attendant was to clear up the mess associated with exploding corpses. Each of the bodies had a bell attached to its fingers, which the attendant had to listen out for. According to reports, these bells would often ring because the corpses would move and expand as they decomposed. No one sent to a waiting mortuary ever woke up.

However, the waiting mortuaries turned out to have another, incidental benefit. As well as removing the risk of premature burial (even though they appear to have had no meaningful success in this area), the waiting mortuaries also removed the corpse from the home of the grieving family. This idea took off, and waiting mortuaries became popular in Germany in the 1800s, providing a place where the corpses would be kept until they showed signs of putre-faction. These establishments were staffed by a matron, nurses and porters. A doctor was also kept on call, should any of the patients show signs of life and every corpse had a comfortable place to sleep.

In Frankfurt am Main, a wealthy man, terrified of being

buried prematurely, donated money to build a luxury waiting mortuary. It consisted of two wards, with 66 beds in total that were constantly observed by nurses and porters. A doctor also made regular daily visits. All the dead bodies wore white gloves and their hands were attached to a powerful gong by a piece of string – if there was any movement, the gong would make a noise.

After the discovery of the heartbeat as a clear sign of life or death, the European fear of being buried prematurely diminished from 1840 onward. The last German waiting mortuaries were closed in the 1890s. Further, the development of embalming and cremation in the late 1800s helped to give people peace of mind about being buried alive.

What is a safety coffin?

Waiting mortuaries were not the only innovations designed to protect people against the risk of premature burial. From the mid-1800s through to the early 1900s, a number of coffin alarm devices were patented. In the 1850s, George Bateson made a lot of money from his very successful safety coffin, which was marketed as the Bateson's Life Revival Device. The device consisted of a bell that was attached by rope, through the lid of the coffin, to the corpse's hands. If the corpse awakened, they could simply ring the bell for assistance. Queen Victoria awarded Bateson the Order of the British Empire for his services to the dead. During the Victorian age, his invention and other coffin bell alarms could be found in many of the new graves in cemeteries far and wide. However, despite the success of his invention, Bateson was driven insane by his obsession with being buried prematurely. Even his own invention didn't allay his fears – he rewrote his will asking to be cremated.

How long could a person survive if buried inside a coffin?

It is perhaps reassuring to know that even if a person were to become trapped inside a coffin, they would not have to endure the experience for very long. Trapped inside a coffin, 1.8m (6ft) underground, a person would quickly exhaust the limited air available. In 1862, the German physiologist Johann Ernst Hebenstreit calculated that there would not be enough air in an average airtight coffin to sustain a person for more than one hour. This claim inspired another scientist, a man named Dr Von Rosser who, in the late 1800s, carried out an experiment in which he placed a dog in an airtight coffin with a glass lid – the unfortunate animal died within three hours. As humans have roughly three times the lung capacity of a dog, Von Rosser was inclined to agree with Hebenstreit's calculation.

Who was the woman who died three times?

Even with all the advances made by medical science today, doctors can still misdiagnose death. In 2000, a documentary called *Premature Burial* was made about the woman who died three times. By the age of 65 Allison Burchell, of Horsham, Sussex, had been pronounced dead on three occasions in her life.

In 1952, when she was 17 years old, she collapsed unconscious in a cinema and was rushed to hospital where she was pronounced dead. However, despite her body being paralysed she was able to see and hear clearly. She was aware of all the conversations being held by the nurses as they prepared her body and eventually took her to the mortuary. Thankfully, after around 30 minutes she recovered and was then subjected to numerous tests, which revealed that she suffered with severe narcolepsy. The disorder has symptoms that include overwhelming drowsiness, sudden attacks of sleep and cataplexy; this is a sudden loss of muscle control that can cause short-term paralysis. Narcolepsy can leave the patient totally paralysed, even though they are fully conscious and able to understand everything that's going on around them.

A few years later, Allison suffered another attack and she woke up in a mortuary surrounded by dead bodies. In the 1970s, she had moved to Melbourne and suffered a third attack. Again, she was pronounced dead, but her teenage son convinced hospital staff not to place her body in the airtight refrigeration unit. Allison described the sensation, 'You can see and hear everything going on around you, but there is no way to convey to anyone that you are not dead. It's the most terrifying thing imaginable.' Thankfully, Allison wasn't put into the refrigeration unit, and once again she made a full recovery.

Why would doctors in the 1700s and 1800s pour warm urine into the mouths of corpses?

A wide range of extraordinary methods was developed to try to ensure that those who appeared to be dead were, in fact, dead before being buried in the ground.

In 1752, Paris physician Antoine Louis suggested blowing tobacco smoke into the corpse's anus. Thankfully, he wasn't proposing actually to blow the smoke himself. Instead, he developed a piece of equipment that resembled a set of bellows with pipes attached, which he enthusiastically demonstrated on corpses in the morgues of Paris. In the 1800s, tobacco enemas were frequently carried out on corpses by doctors in Holland, London and Germany. However, there was never a successful resuscitation reported.

Other methods seemed to assume simply that pain would sort the actual dead from the merely somnolent. An Englishman named Barnett recommended that the arm of the corpse be scalded with boiling water; if a blister resulted, it meant the body was alive. A French clergyman came up with a rather more direct method of ensuring an individual was dead – he recommended thrusting a red-hot poker into the corpse's anus. In 1854, another Frenchman, by the name of Jules-Antoine Josat, invented an innovative device called the *pince-mamelon*, which means nipple-pincher. As you might imagine, this device's job was to squeeze the nipple very hard, causing any living body to wake up due to the intense pain.

A Danish anatomist named Jacob Winslow (1669–1760) invented numerous methods to ensure a person was actually dead, as described below:

> The individual's nostrils are to be irritated by introducing sternutaries, errhines [things that cause sneezing and produce mucus], juices of onions, garlic and horse-radish …The gums are to be rubbed with garlic, and the skin stimulated by the liberal application of whips nettles. The intestines can be irritated by the most acrid enemas, the limbs agitated through violent pulling, and the ears shocked by hideous Shrieks and excessive Noises. Vinegar and salt should be poured in the corpse's mouth and where they cannot be had, it is customary to pour warm Urine into it, which has been observed to produce happy Effects.

Other methods used included poking long needles under the corpse's toenails, pouring boiling wax over its head, slicing its feet with razors, shouting into the corpse's ears, thrusting a sharp pencil up its nose; and a Swedish writer even recommended that a crawling insect be conveyed into the corpse's ear.

In late 1892, French physician Jean Baptiste Vincent Laborde advised tongue pulling, about 15 to 20 times per minute, to be carried out for at least three hours following the supposed death. He even invented a hand-cranked tongue-pulling machine for use in the mortuary. He believed this method was the most effective and successful way of resuscitation as it stimulated the respiratory reflex, and so would help to encourage breathing. He noted its successful use in 63 cases.

However, some doctors realised that the most reliable way to identify the dead was simply to allow the body to decompose for a few days. In 1740, anatomist Jacob Winslow wrote, 'The onset of purification was the only reliable indicator that the subject had died.' This meant that corpses would be left hanging around in doctors' surgeries or in the home. The putrid smell and abundance of insects hovering around the body were sure signs that a person was most probably dead. In 1846, a more scientific way of determining if someone was dead was suggested by a French doctor named Bouchut. Stethoscopes had recently been invented and Bouchut believed that they could be used to determine whether or not the body's heart was beating. If the heart was not beating, this meant the person was indeed dead.

What is the story of Sleeping Beauty really about?

Children everywhere love the famous tale of Sleeping Beauty in which the handsome prince falls in love with the beautiful young girl. However, while many of us think of it as simply a sweet, romantic fairy tale, others derive a rather different meaning. Some psychoanalysts argue that the story of Sleeping Beauty is actually a coded reference to necrophilia: the practice of engaging in sexual acts with dead bodies. The key elements of the story, they argue, are that a beautiful, dead princess is aroused from her permanent slumber by the sexual advances of a handsome prince.

In fact, sexual molestation of the dead has occurred throughout history. In some periods, it appears to have been widespread enough for some societies to take active precautions to prevent it. In ancient Egypt, for example, to ensure that corpses were not dug up and sexually abused, the practice was for bodies to be left to decompose for days before being buried, so that they were sufficiently rotten at the point of burial.

At his court martial in 1849, Sergeant Francois Bertrand of the French army admitted to numerous sexual attacks on corpses. His sick antics were initially confined to digging up corpses until his bare hands bled and then masturbating while touching the corpse's intestines with his hand. Eventually, however, he went a step further and had sexual intercourse with the body of a 16-year-old girl that he had unearthed. He recalls:

> I cannot describe what I felt during that time. But all my enjoyment with living women is nothing as compared with it. I kissed the girl all over her body, I pressed her to my heart as though I wanted to crush her; in short, I did everything to her that a passionate lover does to his mistress. Having enjoyed the body for about a quarter of an hour, I cut it up and, as in the case of my other victims, tore out her intestines.

To satisfy his overwhelming sexual appetite, not only was he carrying out his nightly escapades, but he was also involved in sexual relationships with a large number of actual, living women, several of whom wanted to marry him.

One night, while climbing over a wall into a cemetery, he was severely wounded by a gun booby trap that had been set up specifically to catch him. Nonetheless, this didn't deter the tenacious Francois, and even though he'd been shot, he managed to dig up a female corpse, cut out her genitals and then slash her thighs. Several days later, a gravedigger overheard a soldier mention that one of his comrades had been accidentally wounded a few days before and was in the military hospital. This information led to Bertrand's eventual capture and confession, and he was sent to prison.

In the 1930s a 60-year-old German man, Count Karl Tangler von Cosel (who in fact wasn't a count at all, except in his own mind), lived in Key West, Florida. He worked as an X-ray technician in a local hospital; and one day, he was given the job of X-raying an advanced case of tuberculosis in a 20-year-old Cuban woman called Maria Elena Hoyos. He instantly fell in love and became devastated when she died shortly afterwards. Her family buried Elena in Key West's City Cemetery, but many years later it was discovered that her body was missing. Investigators were shocked to discover Elena's embalmed corpse in von Cosel's shack, reclining on a large bed. Von Cosel had replaced her rotten eyes with glass eyes and reconstructed her face, breasts, arms, legs and trunk – he had even invented a special vaginal tube that allowed sexual intercourse.

Von Cosel confessed to the abduction of the body and spent time in jail. However, many years later, at the time of his death, morticians found an eerie sight propped in the corner of his small shack: a life-size replica of Maria Elena Hoyos.

What was the gruesome fate of Oliver Cromwell's head?

Oliver Cromwell (1599–1658) was the leader of the Parliamentarian army during the English Civil War. His army, the New Model Army, defeated the Royalists, resulting in the execution of King Charles I in 1649. In 1653, Cromwell was offered the title of king by a council of officers, but he turned it down, and instead assumed the title of Lord Protector of England, Scotland and Ireland.

Cromwell died of natural causes in 1658, and he was embalmed and buried with great ceremony in Westminster

Abbey, alongside past kings and queens. However, Cromwell was evidently extremely unpopular at his death, as Royalist John Evelyn described, 'the joyfullest funeral that ever I saw for there was none that cried but dogs'.

However, Cromwell did not rest in peace for long. In 1661, following the restoration of the monarchy, Cromwell was reviled as a regicide and despised by the public for inflicting years of puritanical oppression. Cromwell and two other parliamentary leaders, Henry Ireton and John Bradshaw, were exhumed, and their remains were dragged through the streets of London to Tyburn. Still in shrouds, they were hung from the gallows all day, before being taken down and having the heads severed from their bodies – bodies which would have been in a state of considerable decay after several years in the grave. Cromwell's head was then fixed to a metal pole at Westminster Hall, as a warning to anyone else who might dare to oppose the monarchy. It remained on display there for over 20 years.

In 1660, people who had participated in the trial and execution of Charles I were brought to trial. Ten people were condemned to death and publicly hanged, drawn and quartered in London, and a further 19 were sentenced to life imprisonment.

In the Museum of London, the death mask of Oliver Cromwell clearly shows a wart over the right eye. Cromwell seems to have been quite fond of his warts and is reputed to have said the following to his portrait artist, Sir Peter Lely:

> Mr Lely, I desire you would use all your skill to paint my picture truly like me, and not flatter me at all; but remark all these roughnesses, pimples, warts, and everything as you see me, otherwise I will never pay a farthing for it.

Can medicine be derived from corpses?

The dead have long been seen as potentially useful to the living, especially to help cure illness and prolong lives. From an ancient Egyptian medical text, as far back as 1550 BC, we have records of human brains being cut up and used to cure eye ailments.

In ancient Rome, epileptic patients were often prescribed several doses of human liver that was usually taken from a gladiator, because gladiator livers were considered to be especially strong and courageous. The ancient Roman philosopher Celsus wrote in his book *De Medicina* that epileptics would be cured if they drank the blood of a slain gladiator.

Down the ages, in many different cultures, parts of dead bodies have been used as medicinal cures. For example, a cure for ulcers, goitre, cysts and diseases such as tuberculosis was to touch a dead man's hand, preferably the hand of someone who had died a premature death. Public executions attracted large crowds, and people gathered in the hope that a hangman would let them touch the hand of the still-warm victim as he dangled from the rope – they would even pay the hangman for the privilege. The enterprising executioner at Newgate Prison in London developed a similar and profitable sideline – he chopped off his victims' hands and sold them. Hangmen also made money from selling remedies made of herbs and human fat from their victims.

During the 1600s and 1700s, people in Denmark believed that fresh blood would cure epilepsy. People flocked to public hangings, and they stood by the condemned, in the hope that they'd catch some blood in a cup. In the 1680s, human skulls were sold in London and people would grate them to a fine powder, which they would then consume. In 1721, the Dispensatory of the Royal College of Physicians was recommending 'three drams of human skull' to help epilepsy sufferers, and the *Pharmacopoeia Londinensis* of 1618, which was an encyclopaedia of medicine and drugs, recommended powdered human skull for epilepsy. In German folk medicine, it was advised that woman in labour should wear strips of tanned human skin as belts to ease the pain of giving birth.

The incredibly well-preserved state of Egyptian mummies led European doctors from the Middle Ages onwards to sell mummy parts as medication. In the 1100s, European doctors ground mummies into a powder, which they advised was to be drunk as a tea or used in a poultice for its numerous health benefits. It was prescribed for many ailments including coughs, nausea, epilepsy, migraines, incontinence, gout, bruises and even fractures! When mummies were in short supply, unscrupulous mummy suppliers quickly mummified the bodies of executed prisoners to be sold as ancient mummies.

However, unsurprisingly, there is no evidence that eating any part of a mummy can actually help cure any ailment, so it's astonishing that its use continued until the seventeenth century. It fell out of favour mainly because of the problems associated with consuming it. French surgeon Ambrose Pare wrote that, 'not only does this wretched drug do no good, but it causes great pain to the stomach, gives foul-smelling breath, and brings on serious vomiting'.

King Charles II (1630–85) used powder from Egyptian mummies and rubbed it onto his skin all over his body. He believed it would promote longevity and transmit ancient greatness.

Why did Evita's corpse spend time in a wooden crate?

Eva Peron (1919–52), who was popularly known as Evita, was the wife of the Argentinian president Juan Peron. In 1952, at just 33, she tragically died of cancer. Juan was so heartbroken about her death that he spent over £50,000 having her embalmed. The man entrusted with this project was Dr Pedro Ara, who spent a year embalming Evita. The operation involved endless injections of chemicals and placing the body into baths of acetate and potassium nitrate. He even applied layers of transparent plastic onto her face. When he had finished, it was said that she looked even better than she had in real life.

Peron had planned to build a mausoleum in Evita's honour, so that her body could be put on permanent public display. However, this plan was thwarted when his government was overthrown in 1955 by the army's General Aramburu, who led a successful coup against the government. Many army officers, who initially professed loyalty to the government, had lost in confidence in Peron and showed little enthusiasm for defending his regime. Leaving Evita's body behind, Peron was forced to flee Argentina and then to Spain where he lived in exile in Madrid.

Because of Evita's enduring popularity, the new government didn't know what to do with the body, and so for security reasons they moved it several times. People protested and became extremely militant, demanding to view her enshrined body. Fearful of insurrection, General

Aramburu arranged to smuggle her body out of the country and shipped it to Italy. For a while, the body was hidden in the apartment of an Argentinian army major. Later, it was hidden in a wooden crate labelled 'radio equipment' and stored in the attic of military intelligence headquarters. In 1957 the body was sent to a cemetery in Milan, and was buried with the name Maria Maggi on the tomb.

Fuelled by the mystery over the missing body, rumours began to circulate that Evita was still alive. In 1969, Aramburu was assassinated, and the continuing political unease eventually led to the restoration of Juan Peron to the presidency in 1973. Two years earlier, the location of Evita's body had been discovered, and it was then exhumed and smuggled to Madrid to join Peron and his new wife Isabelita. Dr Ara was summoned once again, and the casket was opened with a crowbar. In his memoirs, Ara claimed that Evita's body was in good condition, except for some minor damage. However, in a statement released in 1985, Evita's two sisters contradicted Dr Ara's account. They said that gross mistreatment of their sister's remains included hammer blows to the temple and forehead, an almost severed neck, a sunken nose and broken septum, cuts on the cheek, chest and arm, an amputated finger, fractured kneecaps and a layer of tar on the soles of her feet. Nonetheless, Dr Ara restored the body, and in 1976, Evita was buried for the last time in a vault in Buenos Aires, in the company of 13 presidents of Argentina.

Is it possible to turn dead bodies into diamonds?

LifeGem, a company based in the US, with an office in the UK, is able to turn human ashes into diamonds. However, this service is by no means cheap – it can cost the customer around £13,000. The process takes around 16 weeks and involves heating the ashes up to a temperature of 3,000° C (5,432° F), which converts the carbon in the ashes into graphite. Pressure is then applied to the graphite, turning it into a diamond. In fact, there is enough carbon in the average human body to make a necklace and a pair of earrings. LifeGem can also obtain carbon from a lock of hair. This means that they can even create diamonds from people who prefer to have their bodies buried. The diamonds can be cut into various shapes and made into different colours including blue, white, red, green and yellow. They can even create diamonds from the ashes of your favourite moggy or pooch.

What gruesome event occurred while making an episode of *The Six Million Dollar Man*?

In 1977, while filming *The Six Million Dollar Man* at the Nu-Pike Amusement Park in Long Beach, California, one of crew was instructed to move a mannequin that was painted fluorescent orange, dressed as a cowboy and dangling from a rope. Unfortunately, as the crew member tried to lift the body down, one of its arms broke off, and the crew were horrified to discover that the mannequin was in fact a human corpse. The cowboy dummy turned out to be the embalmed body of Elmer McCurdy (1880–1911).

Amazingly, thanks to items found in McCurdy's mouth – a 1924 penny and a ticket from the Museum of Crime in Los Angeles – investigators were able to piece together his life story. McCurdy was a low-level criminal, who bragged that he had killed a man in a brawl but whose only arrest was for being drunk in Kansas. After a variety of jobs, McCurdy decided to turn to robbing trains. In 1911 he travelled to Oklahoma and ambushed a train that he believed contained thousands of dollars of government tribal payments. In fact it was just a passenger train and he got away with just US$46 and two jugs of whiskey. As law enforcers closed in, he warned them that he would not be taken alive. They quickly proved him right, as he was shot to death in the resulting shoot-out.

McCurdy's body was taken to a funeral parlour in Oklahoma. Nobody came forward to claim the body, and so the undertaker came up with an ingenious idea – he charged customers a nickel to see The Bandit Who Wouldn't Give Up. Some time later, the undertaker was conned by two people who claimed to be relatives of McCurdy; they wanted the body so that they could give him a proper and respectful send-off. The undertaker reluctantly handed over the body, which the conmen then used as an exhibit in a travelling carnival. Eventually, McCurdy's body ended up at the Nu-Pike Amusement Park, where it was stored and forgotten, until the film crew discovered the unusually life-like mannequin. Once the mystery had been unravelled,

McCurdy's body was returned to Oklahoma and buried in a cemetery in 1977. The state medical examiner ordered that two cubic yards of concrete be poured over McCurdy's coffin, so that his remains would never be disturbed again.

How did a nosebleed kill the Scourge of God?

Attila the Hun (AD 403–53) was renowned as one of the most fearsome warriors in history, earning himself the soubriquet the Scourge of God. Ancient writers describe Attila's physical appearance as, 'a large head, a swarthy complexion, small, deep-seated eyes, a flat nose, a few hairs in the place of a beard, broad shoulders and a short square body'. Attila may have been no oil painting, but he had an impressive party trick: he could roll his eyes around and around in his head really fast. However, as befits a bloodthirsty warrior, his favourite hobby was hunting animals and then disembowelling them.

The Huns were a nomadic tribe that originated in central Asia in the fourth century AD and who then settled in

Eastern Europe. Legend has it that when a baby boy was born, in order to help him get accustomed to pain, a cut was made on the face. They were expert horse riders, and could eat and sleep in their saddles. When they galloped into towns, they stole whatever they could and killed anyone in their way, including women and children.

The Hun empire was the largest in Europe at the time, stretching from central Asia as far west as Germany. After their uncle Ruga, the King of the Huns, died in 434, Attila and his brother Bleda ascended to the throne and became joint rulers of the Huns. However, Attila preferred to rule alone, so he arranged a hunting accident for his brother. Attila was now the sole leader of the Huns, and under his leadership the tribe terrorised the whole of Europe. When he conquered a city, Attila liked to display severed heads outside it.

On one of his wedding nights, Attila got very drunk – in fact, this happened a lot, as he reportedly had 300 wives. However, on this occasion, he became so drunk that when he got a nosebleed after falling over, he choked to death on the blood. Rather than cry, the Huns mourned the loss of their leader by cutting off their hair and slashing their bodies with knives; they also cut their cheeks so that they could cry tears of blood. After he was buried, the Huns executed the people who had buried him, so that his grave would never be discovered.

Why was Lenin embalmed?

Vladimir Ilyich Lenin (1870–1924) was the Russian leader who, along with Leon Trotsky, led the Bolshevik revolution that toppled the Czarist Russian government in 1917. His leadership came to an end after he suffered a succession of strokes that ultimately led to his death. Following his demise, Lenin's brain was removed, preserved and then sliced up into thousands of sections. It was then analysed by scientists, whose aim was to prove that he had an extra-ordinary mind. Some pieces even found their way to Germany during the Second World War, where the Nazis carried out their own tests on sections of Lenin's brain.

The rest of Lenin's body was put on display, and over half a million people queued for hours in freezing temper-atures to view his corpse. After witnessing the massive public response and the palpable grief, Lenin's successor, Josef Stalin (1878–1953), realised the propaganda value of putting his dead predecessor's body on permanent display. He believed this would to keep the revolution on track.

For two months, doctors Boris Zbarsky and Vladimir Vorobiov worked night and day to preserve the body, so that it looked as it had done in life. They knew that failure would mean certain death and so, perhaps unsurprisingly, they became world leaders in embalming methods. Mum-mification was achieved through soaking the body in baths of balsam, glycerine and potassium acetate. Ever since, Lenin's remarkably well-preserved body has been housed in a mausoleum in Moscow's Red Square, and it is checked regularly for deterioration. The body is dressed in a new suit every year and has a yearly immersion in preserving chemicals. However, it has often been rumoured that the body is actually made of wax.

After his death, Stalin was embalmed and displayed alongside Lenin. However, the brutality of Stalin's regime was repudiated by his successor, Nikita Khrushchev, and in 1961 Stalin's embalmed body was put into a coffin and buried by the Kremlin Wall.

Where can you find a bone chapel?

If you fancy a gruesome family day out, why not visit the Chapel of Skulls in Czermna, Poland? As its name suggests, this church displays many bones; in fact, it is decorated with 3,000 skulls and other bones that line the chapel walls. The ceiling is densely covered with hundreds of human skulls, each positioned above two crossed leg bones. There are over 20,000 more skulls stored in the vaults. The chapel was the innovative idea of a local Czech parish priest, who created it in 1776, to act as a memorial to those who had lost their lives in the wars of the 1600s and 1700s. This popular attraction also contains the bones of some of the victims of the many cholera epidemics that plagued the area.

Another macabre chapel, called the Capela dos Ossos or Bone Chapel, can be found in Evora, Portugal. It was built in the fifteenth century by Franciscan monks, and measures

18.7m (61ft 4in) long and 11m (36ft) wide, with three small windows and eight pillars. The chapel is decorated with human bones and skulls from around 5,000 bodies taken from local cemeteries. They are held together by cement and can be found covering the walls and pillars of the chapel. The chapel also contains two dried-out leathery corpses hanging from the ceiling – their identities are unknown.

Beneath the city of Rome lie hundreds of tunnels dug out of the soft volcanic rock. These extend for miles and contain the buried remains of tens of thousands of people. Rows of tightly packed bones are piled from the floor to the ceiling and have remained there for almost 2,000 years. In the second century, Christians started burying their dead underground, and the catacombs continued to function as cemeteries until the fifth century. The bones mostly belong to Christians, but the catacombs also house the bones of Jews and pagans. Burials of early Christians involved wrapping the body in a sheet or shroud and placing it into a niche cut out of the rock. The niche would then be sealed with tiles and fixed with mortar or a slab of marble, upon which the name of the deceased would sometimes be engraved. Some of the tunnels are open to the public for guided tours.

What is promession?

Cremation was introduced in response to the growing shortage of available land for burial; the first legal cremation was carried out in the Cremation Society's crematorium at Woking, Surrey in 1885. The cremation process has progressed from the first coke-fired ovens to more modern gas and electric cremators over the last 100 years. Nowadays, almost all crematoria use gas, but unfortunately this pollutes the environment. Ovens in the crematoria burn for around an hour and a half per body, at temperatures of up to 1,1000°C (2,0120°F), using up the same amount of energy as a typical home would in a month. The burning of wooden coffins also causes harmful emissions to be released in the atmosphere. Another problem is that the dental fillings found in the teeth of the cremated can emit mercury and contaminate the environment. However, crematoria are now being fitted with special filters to eliminate this problem. Still, if you're hoping for an eco-friendly death, there is a greener way to dispose of your earthly remains.

Susanne Wiigh-Masak, an enterprising environmental biologist from Sweden, has come up with an eco-friendly alternative to cremation with a method known as promession. This process involves submerging the corpse in liquid nitrogen, which causes the body to become brittle. It is then vibrated in a machine, where it shatters into millions of pieces. While the machine vibrates, a metal separator is used to find items such as metal plates, dental fillings and hip-replacement parts. Eventually, all that is left is a powdery substance, which is then placed into a box made of corn or potato starch that can then be buried in a shallow grave. The box and its contents will then turn into compost over a period of around six to 12 months. Often, relatives choose to plant a tree or shrub at the grave site to make a pleasingly green use of the compost.

What was Alistair Cooke's last big story?

Alistair Cooke (1908–2004) was a renowned journalist and broadcaster, who was perhaps best known for *Letter from America*, a weekly 15-minute radio programme that was broadcast on BBC Radio Four and the World Service from 1946 to 2004 – it was the world's longest-running speech radio programme. Each week, Cooke dealt with a topical American issue, often in an anecdotal and humorous fashion. Cooke was educated at Jesus College, Cambridge, but later in life he became a naturalised American citizen and lived in a rent-controlled Manhattan apartment for over 50 years. In March 2004, Cooke died at his home in New York. He was cremated, and his ashes were scattered in Central Park.

In December 2005, the *New York Daily News* reported that Cooke's bones had been removed from his corpse, prior to cremation, by the staff of Biomedical Tissue Services (BTS), a tissue-recovery company based in Fort Lee, New Jersey. The report revealed that the company was being investigated for a range of gruesome practices involving the illegal recovery of human bones and tissues.

The company had been taking body parts from funeral homes, often paying the homes US$1,000 or more per corpse, and selling the parts to transplant companies around the world for dental implants, hip replacements and other procedures. BTS would forge family consent and other donor forms, often going against the family's expressed wishes. They also engaged in a number of unusual and unsafe practices, including failing to screen body parts for diseases such as HIV/AIDS. In one case, the company replaced the bones of a woman from Queens, New York, with PVC piping, to trick members of her family.

Alistair Cooke had died at the age of 95 from lung cancer, which had spread to his bones, but this did not prevent BTS from selling his bones on for use in bone grafts, even though the cancer meant they were unsuitable for this type of therapy. The company had removed his bones the day after he died and sold them on for US$11,000. He was only considered a suitable donor because BTS had lied about the cause of death, listing it as a heart attack, rather than cancer. They also claimed that Cooke was 85 when he died, not 95. Fortunately, thanks to the police investigation, Cooke's bones were never implanted in anyone, and his remains were given to the family for cremation.

In February 2006, Dr Michael Mastromarino, the head of BTS, was convicted, along with three employees, of stealing body parts from around 1,400 corpses. Mastromarino was sentenced in June 2008 to between 25 and 58 years in prison.

Which Hollywood star was kidnapped after his death?

When Hollywood legend and star of silent films Charlie Chaplin (1889–1977) died, he was laid to rest in Switzerland. However, three months later, his widow Oona received a strange phone call from a man demanding US$600,000 for Charlie's body to be returned to her. She made enquiries, and indeed it was true that Charlie Chaplin's body had been stolen. One night, two people had broken into the cemetery at Corsier-sur-Vevey, dug up his body, and carried it away.

Oona contacted the police, and they tapped her phone line. She continued to maintain contact with the body-snatchers but refused to pay the ransom. After several more calls, the criminals reduced the ransom down to US$250,000, but by this point the police had traced them to a phone in Lausanne. The kidnapper turned out to be a 24-year-old Polish car mechanic who, together with a friend, admitted to stealing the body. The two men were sent to prison, and Charlie Chaplin's body was reburied in a steel vault under 1.8m (6ft) of concrete, to ensure that it would not happen again.

Why was the tomb of St Thomas Becket at Canterbury one of England's most popular pilgrimage sites?

Thomas Becket (1118–1170) was born in Cheapside, London, to the prosperous London merchant Gilbert Becket. Through his father's wealthy connections, Becket received an excellent education in London, Paris, Bologna and Auxerre. On his return to England, he became an agent for the Archbishop of Canterbury, Theobald, who sent him on several important missions to Rome. Becket was clearly an impressive young man, as Theobald recommended him to the king, Henry II. Henry made Becket his Lord Chancellor, and the two became close friends. Henry was determined to reduce the power of the Church, and used Becket to enforce land taxes against the clergy. After the death of Theobald in 1162, Henry appointed Becket to the post of Archbishop of Canterbury.

Until this point, Becket had been a fun-loving courtier, but after his appointment he became an ascetic, which meant he pursued a simple, serious-minded life, devoted to his faith and abstaining from worldly pleasures. A rift developed between Becket and Henry, as it became clear that Becket would not be the puppet Archbishop Henry had hoped for; instead he would defend the Church's interests and wealth. At the assemblies at Clarendon Palace in 1164, Henry demanded that Becket sign documents recognising the King's authority over the Church, but Becket refused. This meant the two power bases were now effectively at war, and Becket was forced to flee to the continent, where he remained in exile for several years. Nonetheless, he continued to cause trouble for Henry, and when, in 1170, Becket excommunicated three leading bishops, Henry was reported to have lifted his head from his sickbed and moaned, 'Will no one rid me of this troublesome priest?' Four of Henry's knights interpreted this as a royal command and brutally murdered Becket at Canterbury Cathedral, in a crime that shocked Christian Europe. Becket soon became regarded across Europe as a religious martyr, and just three years after his death he was canonised by Pope Alexander III.

In the years that followed, Becket's tomb at St Dunstan's, Canterbury, became one of the most popular pilgrimage sites in England. Holy tourism was a lucrative business for the Church, and Becket's tomb was particularly appealing for a number of reasons. Firstly, it was much easier to get to than Rome or Santiago de Compostela, being a reasonably short journey from London; and because of Becket's status, the indulgences or religious benefits were just as great. Secondly, the pilgrimage route was an interesting and relevant one, as it traced Becket's final journey, from St Mary's Priory in Southwark, where he gave his last sermon, past landmarks such as Becket's Well in Otford, Kent, where Becket was said to have created two natural springs by striking the ground with his crosier. The third reason for the tomb's enormous appeal was surely that it was extremely and fascinatingly gruesome. Becket's death had been a violent one, and visitors to Canterbury could actually get to see where the sword had split his skull in two!

How much coffee would it take to kill a man?

According to legend, coffee was discovered in the ninth century by a goatherder named Kaldi in Abyssinia (present-day Ethiopia). Kaldi is said to have noticed that his goats became unusually lively after eating the berries from a particular shrub, so he decided to try the berries himself, and found that he too became more alert and energetic. This was, of course, because the berries were coffee beans which contain the stimulant caffeine. Caffeine is the world's most widely used psychoactive substance.

In moderate doses, caffeine is harmless, and can even have beneficial effects. Studies have shown that cyclists and runners who have consumed caffeine can perform at a competitive pace for significantly longer periods and distances. However, excessive use of caffeine over time can lead to a condition called caffeinism, whose symptoms can include muscle twitching, headaches, hyperventilation, insomnia and heart palpitations.

It is also possible to overdose on caffeine, which can lead to a wide range of symptoms including flushing, nervousness, increased urination, delirium, muscle twitching and an irregular heartbeat. Extreme cases of caffeine overdose can even cause death, but this would be very unlikely to happen through drinking coffee alone. To cause a fatal overdose, a person would need to consume more than 5g (⅛oz) of caffeine, which would mean drinking around 80 to 100 cups of coffee within a period of about four to five hours. There have been reported cases of deaths from caffeine overdose, but these were believed to have been caused by caffeine pills.

Can a person die of a broken heart?

James Callaghan (1912–2005) and Audrey Moulton met while they were in their teens, at the Baptist church where they both taught at Sunday school. They married in 1938, and Callaghan went on to become the only man to hold all four of the great offices of state in the UK: Prime Minister, Chancellor of the Exchequer, Home Secretary and Foreign Secretary. When, in her later years, Audrey developed Alzheimer's disease, Callaghan devoted himself to her care, saying, 'For sixty years she gave up everything for me, and now I'm going to give up everything for her.' She died on 15 March 2005, and Callaghan followed just 11 days later.

Could Callaghan have died of a broken heart? In 1969, a study was published in the *British Medical Journal*. Scientists had monitored 4,500 widows for nine years after their husbands died, and they found that the widows were 40 per cent more likely to die within the six months after their spouse's death. After that period, the risk slowly fell back to normal levels. Most of the widows had died of a heart attack. Numerous studies have since confirmed that people are more at risk of death in the months following the loss of a spouse, and that there is an increased risk of heart disorders.

In 2005, researchers at Johns Hopkins University in

Baltimore found that sudden emotional stress could cause a condition called acute-stress cardiomyopathy or broken-heart syndrome. The researchers examined 19 patients, mostly women in their sixties and seventies, who were all displaying symptoms of conventional heart attacks but with a number of key differences. Normally, heart attacks are caused by damage to the heart muscle, but these patients showed no heart-tissue damage. None of them had a history of heart problems or chronic stress, and all of them had just received some kind of emotional trauma or sudden shock, including a death in the family, an armed robbery, and, in one case, a surprise birthday party. Each of the patients had unusually high levels of stress hormones in their blood, and the researchers determined that it was these hormones, including adrenaline, that were impairing the heart's ability to pump.

> Ah, what a trifle is a heart,
> If once into love's hands it come!

John Donne (1532–1631), 'The Broken Heart'

What happened when William the Conqueror's corpse was placed in his tomb?

William the Conqueror (1028–87) became King William I following his victory at the battle of Hastings in 1066. As a young adult, William was so fit that he could jump onto his horse when dressed in full armour. However, later in life he piled on the pounds and became grossly overweight.

When King Philip I of France made some spiteful comments about William being too fat, William set fire to the small French town of Mantes in France. As the fire burnt, his horse stepped on a hot cinder and slipped. This caused William to be thrown forward and fall onto the point of this saddle. He sustained a nasty injury that caused internal bleeding, and six weeks later he died.

As William was already large and the decomposition of his body caused it to swell, it became too big to fit inside the stone tomb. Legend has it that two soldiers had to stand on the body to push it in. In their desperation to cram it in, they jumped up and down on the body and broke its spine. The broken spine pierced the stomach, and because of the accumulation of gases it exploded, splattering the poor soldiers with rotting flesh. The smell was so putrid that everyone, including priests, rushed out of the church to get some fresh air.

Index

INDEX